A M?Culloch   Nov 09

GW00995311

The Honey Bee Inside Out

THE Honey Bee INSIDE OUT

Celia F Davis

Bee Craft Limited

© 2004 Celia F Davis, reprinted 2006

All rights reserved. No part of this publication may be reproduced, stored in a retrieval system, or transmitted, in any form or by any means, electronic, mechanical, photocopying, recording, or otherwise, without the prior written permission of the publisher.

A catalogue record for this book is available from the British Library

ISBN 0-900147-07-5

Published in Great Britain by
Bee Craft Limited
National Beekeeping Centre
Stoneleigh-park
Stoneleigh
Warwickshire
CV8 2LG

Typeset by Buzzwords Editorial Ltd, Little Addington, Northamptonshire, and Digimagination, Oldham, Lancashire

Printed in Great Britain by
Cambrian Printers, Aberystwyth

ACKNOWLEDGEMENTS

Diagrams on pages 10, 32, 35, 40, 50 and 85 redrawn from *The Anatomy and Physiology of the Honey Bee*, HA Dade, with kind permission of the publishers, IBRA, 18 North Road, Cardiff.
Diagrams on pages 58, 82, 83 and 84 redrawn from *Anatomy of the Honey Bee*, RE Snodgrass, with kind permission of the publishers, Cornell University Press Ltd, London, UK.
Diagram on page 45 redrawn from *The Insects: structure and function* by RF Chapman, with kind permission of the publishers, Cambridge University Press, Cambridge, UK.
Diagram on page 54 redrawn from *The Insects: structure and function* by RF Chapman. Taken from: Goldsmith, T H (1962) 'Fine structure of the retinulae in the compound eye of the honey-bee'. *Journal of Cell Biology*, **14**, 489–94, with kind permission of Rockefeller University Press.

Photographs by Celia and Cyril Davis except for those on page 77 (Adrian Waring), pages 97, 100, 104, 108, 136(a) and 138(a) (Claire Waring) and page 138(b) (J Velik).

CONTENTS

PREFACE

The aim of this book is to present, in a readable and easily understandable form, the structural and functional biology, and the behaviour of the honey bee. When, at the invitation of the editor, I began writing for *Bee Craft* a few years ago, I envisaged just a few articles, but I am still writing them seven years later. My remit was to make them relevant to the BBKA Examinations and understandable to the non-biologist. I have now been persuaded to put some of them together so that they are accessible both to students and others, who are interested in what makes a honey bee tick. This book is the result. In preparing the text I have added many diagrams which did not appear in the articles. I have drawn most of these directly from bee specimens or from my own dissections. Where diagrams from other publications have been used, the source has been acknowledged.

I would like to thank a number of people who have assisted with this project. First, the staff of Bee Craft Ltd and its editorial team, particularly Claire Waring, who has worked unstintingly throughout to bring this book to publication and without whose encouragement it would never have been written, Janet Pattison who translated my hand-drawn efforts into usable diagrams, and Alison Mouser who worked away quietly to resolve various problems which arose. Their efforts have been invaluable

My daughter and beekeeping partner, Sarah, spent some of her precious spare time reading the early drafts and providing constructive criticism, and Norman Carreck, of Rothamsted Research, was very generous with his time and suggested many improvements.

I would like to register my thanks to my husband, Cyril, who is forced to share his life with bees and has provided much help, advice and encouragement whenever I needed them and finally, although they never read books, I must record the debt of gratitude that I owe to all those bees who have taught me so much over many years and have sometimes, unfortunately, had to make the ultimate sacrifice in my pursuit of knowledge.

Celia F Davis, NDB
March 2004

FOREWORD

Beekeepers are a very varied group of people and I never cease to be amazed by the wide range of backgrounds and skills that they possess. There is, however, no escaping the fact that the keeping of an insect for agricultural production requires a considerable amount of biological knowledge and many who lack formal biological training feel inhibited from attempting the examinations.

The honey bee is probably the most studied of all the insects, so there are a number of excellent books available which cover different aspects of bee biology, but these inevitably presuppose a certain amount of prior biological knowledge. In addition, while considerable advances in bee biology have taken place in recent years, *Anatomy and Dissection of the Honey Bee* by HA Dade, was first published more than 40 years ago, and the most recent edition of the definitive monograph, *Anatomy of the Honey Bee,* by RE Snodgrass, was published in 1956.

Thirty years ago, the UK had a formal system for beekeeping education with professional beekeeping lecturers employed by agricultural colleges in most counties. With financial cutbacks, and beekeeping being increasingly seen as a 'hobby' rather than as an agricultural enterprise, none now remain. Numbers of honey bee colonies and beekeepers declined throughout the twentieth century, such that in some areas of the country, inadequate pollination of crops and wild plants has become a real possibility. In recent years, however, with growing interest in 'green issues' and rural crafts, there are signs of a welcome revival of interest in beekeeping.

While government does recognise the contribution that beekeeping makes to the national economy in terms of the pollination of crops and production of hive products, it is clear that the days of state-funded beekeeping education are over and that beekeeping education must be self supporting. The British

Beekeepers' Association (BBKA) examinations and the National Diploma in Beekeeping (NDB) have adapted themselves to this new era. The BBKA examinations have been redesigned on a modular system so that those with full-time jobs, family and other commitments can obtain their qualifications over a number of years, while the NDB, originally intended as a qualification for county beekeeping lecturers, remains vitally important for those teaching others.

This book, therefore, fills an important gap. Since 1997, Celia Davis has been contributing a series of very readable articles to the journal *Bee Craft* on biological aspects of beekeeping. Many people have suggested that they should be collected together and published in book form, and this volume is the result. While very suitable for those thinking of attempting the various examinations, I am certain that all beekeepers will find this book useful. Drawing on her teaching experience, Celia has trawled through a huge volume of literature and produced a work which should be easily understood by all. Her diagrams, mostly drawn from her own dissections, clearly show what the reader might expect to see down his or her own microscope, rather than idealised representations. The introduction, appendix and glossary with their explanations of biological terminology and scientific nomenclature will prove particularly valuable to those without previous biological training.

Many practical beekeeping texts tend to resemble recipe books, with a list of instructions for what to do in certain circumstances. When the bees, not having read the book, behave differently from that which the author intended, the reader may become totally lost and confused. It is only by clearly understanding the underlying biology that a beekeeper can adapt to manage bees under unfamiliar situations and circumstances. This is the difference between somebody who can follow a recipe and somebody who can actually cook. In this book, Celia has provided the means to turn a bee owner into a beekeeper.

Norman L Carreck, NDB
Rothamsted Research
Harpenden
Hertfordshire
AL5 2JQ

INTRODUCTION

BIOLOGICAL BASICS

Did you learn any biology at school? Can you remember any biology you ever learned? Did your biology lessons ever get past *Amoeba*? If the answer to any of these is 'No' and you want to understand how the honey bee ticks, then this introduction is for you. If you were a whiz in biology lessons and can remember it all as if it were yesterday, then you can skip this and start at Chapter 1. In this introduction, I want to get back to basics and look at the honey bee as a whole unit. The information could just as easily relate to a fish, a bird, or you, or any other multicellular animal you care to think of.

An animal is like a car (well, in some ways)

We all know that, in order to function, a car needs fuel. The fuel has to be burned, which needs oxygen. The result of the burning process is to release the energy which was stored in the fuel. This energy is then used, by the engine, to do work such as moving the wheels. There are waste products produced, exhaust gases and other nasties, which have to be removed from the engine. An animal is fundamentally the same but with refinements:

- Mouthparts get the food/fuel into the animal and the digestive system changes it, if necessary, so that it is soluble in water.
- The circulatory system containing the blood/haemolymph transports the soluble food/fuel to all parts of the body where it is absorbed by the individual cells.
- The respiratory system gets air, containing oxygen, into the body through a system of openings and tubes, so that it, too, can be transported to the cells.

- Energy from the food/fuel is released in the cells when the oxygen and the food/fuel combine together. (This is a very intricate process which ensures that the energy is released in small, usable packages.)

The released energy is either used immediately, for all the processes that go on inside cells to enable the animal to live, or stored in a readily accessible form for future use. The sum of all these processes is called metabolism and it is worth stressing that, even at total rest, an animal still uses up energy to keep its basic body functions going. When it is active, then a great deal more energy is needed and more fuel and oxygen is necessary to produce it, or the stored products can be used.

Waste products are formed as a result of metabolism and these have to be removed from the animal's body, otherwise they would poison it. The blood/haemolymph carries these waste products away from the cells.

The excretory system extracts the waste products from the blood and passes them outside the body.

Complications!

The nervous system is essential to an animal such as the honey bee. It needs it to find its food and to cope with the changes in the surroundings and any dangers which it encounters on the way. Most sense organs are grouped near the front of the insect since it is this part which 'meets' the various stimuli first. Modern cars are catching up here with various sensors which activate systems on the vehicle.

Enzymes. In the engine of our car, the changes which took place did so at a high temperature but, in an animal, thousands of chemical reactions have to proceed constantly at a comparatively low temperature. The reactions therefore need help and this is given in the form of enzymes. These are protein substances which are present in only small quantities but enable the chemical changes to take place rapidly. Each reaction needs its own specific enzyme and most of these are found inside cells.

Growth, regeneration and reproduction. The car uses its fuel to release energy but, as it is used, parts wear out or rust away and it is unable to renew or replace them itself. It is also unable to produce baby cars, even if you lock it up in a dark garage with another car of the same sort! Animals, on the other hand, are able to grow, renew worn out parts to some extent, produce substances which are necessary to proper functioning and make new individuals like themselves. To do all these things they need basic building materials and these come principally from protein foods which they consume. In the case of the honey bee, this means pollen. The proteins go through the same processes as the energy food, being broken down to their constituent parts, which are amino acids. These are then transported to all parts of the body and used to build new proteins which the animal needs.

Keep it simple

It is easy to get bogged down in the minutiae of all the bits and pieces that go to make up a complex animal such as a honey bee. While the detail is essential to a full understanding of how the insect functions, and this is what this book is about, it is important to keep an overall view and to understand that all the parts have developed in response to a need and, more importantly, they do not act in isolation, but as a whole.

1 THE EXTERNAL BODYWORK

FOUNDATIONS

Before we begin to look at the structure, both external and internal, of the honey bee we need to understand some very basic ideas:

A *cell* is a small unit made up (usually) of one nucleus embedded in cytoplasm (collectively called protoplasm) surrounded by a thin cell membrane. The cell membrane allows some substances to pass through it but not others. Cells may be different shapes and sizes depending on their function. The cell is the basic living building block from which an animal like the honey bee is built.

A *tissue* is a collection of, usually, similar cells performing a set function. The cells may be in close contact with one another or they may be separated, with the spaces filled with hard or fluid material.

An *organ* is a collection of tissues carrying out a particular job. Examples of organs are the brain and the ovary.

Now we have that out of the way, we can begin to look at how our favourite insect is made and how it functions.

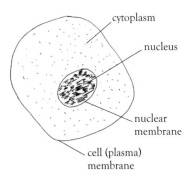

cytoplasm

nucleus

nuclear membrane

cell (plasma) membrane

A typical animal cell

The cytoplasm contains many structures called organelles (literally 'little organs'). These do particular jobs within the cell. The chromosomes are normally dispersed in the nucleus. The nuclear and cell membranes allow some substances to pass through

THE EXOSKELETON

Have you ever paused to think about all those insect specimens in museum cabinets? Some of them have been there for more than 100 years and are still capable of being used as reference specimens for identification. That is quite extraordinary. It is due entirely to the nature of the insects' outer covering which is a non-living, very strong structure. This chapter is going to look at this thick skin of the adult bee, its functions, and how it is built into the insect with which we are so familiar. Just a word about the

The worker honey bee is about 13 mm long and covered by a hard exoskeleton

names – it may be called the body wall, the skin, the integument or the exoskeleton.

Layers and plates

The diagram shows the layers of the body wall of an insect. We can see that there is a single layer of living cells, called the *epidermis*. This produces the thick *cuticle* which is the outer covering of the insect, is non-living and is divided into three layers:

- *Endocuticle* containing a large amount of *chitin*. This is tough but reasonably flexible.
- *Exocuticle*, which is immediately outside the endocuticle, containing some chitin but also a large amount of a substance called *sclerotin*. This makes the layer very hard and dark in colour.
- *Epicuticle* which is the very thin outer layer also containing sclerotin but with no chitin.

(For those of you who are real gluttons for punishment, chitin is derived from glucose, with some nitrogen, built into long chains. It is fibrous. Sclerotin is derived from protein. The chains of

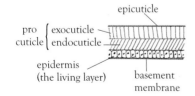

The body wall

(*procuticle + epicuticle = cuticle*)

polypeptides are connected to make a very hard substance which fills in between the chitin fibres in the exocuticle. The epicuticle, although thin, is made up of several layers with different properties.)

Although it is continuous over the bee's body, the cuticle is not uniform. The exocuticle and epicuticle together form plates called *sclerites* which may be fused together but may move relative to one another because the endocuticle forms membranous connections between them. There are different types of sclerite, named according to their positions on the insect:

- *tergum* (pl. terga) – one of the plates situated on the dorsal (back or top) side of the bee
- sternum (pl. sterna) – a plate situated on the bee's ventral (lower or front) side
- pleuron (pl. pleura) – a plate found on the side of the bee between a tergum and a sternum.

In addition to plates covering the outside of the bee, there are extensions of the sclerites inwards into the body cavity. These are called *apodemes* and may be long ridges, pegs or narrow extensions. The apodemes act as attachments for muscles or provide additional strength to the bee's body. The position of an apodeme is marked on the outside of the sclerite by a groove called a *sulcus* or, in the case of a peg, by a pit.

Functions of the cuticle

- To give a waterproof, protective covering.
- To provide anchorage for muscles, allowing the insect to move. This is why it is often called an exoskeleton.
- To make hard structures such as the mouthparts and sting.
- To provide a lining for some 'internal' structures such as the tracheae.

Division into segments

Insects are characteristically divided into sections called segments. In the bee, it is easy to see the segmentation in the abdomen but not in the thorax. The head is not normally recognised as being segmented, except by entomologists who can point to its early embryonic development in primitive insects. When we look at the segmentation, we name each segment using a letter to denote 'thorax' (T) or 'abdomen' (A). The segments are numbered starting at the head end. At least all that is logical and easy to remember!

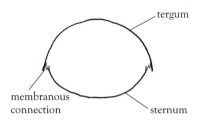

Abdominal segment
(includes the propodeum)

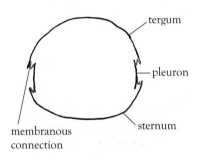

Thoracic segment
It is difficult to see the structure in the thorax of the bee because the segments are modified

Simple diagrams to show the arrangement of the sclerites

notum of T2
scutellum
scutum   scutal
                    fissure
notum of T3
                                                  notum of T1
tergum of
A1   cover over 1st
root of   spiracle (on T2)
hind wing
                            pleuron   tegula - a flap
                            of T2   covering the root
                                                  of the forewing
                                                  foreleg
hind leg   pleuron   mid leg   root of forewing
              of T3

Simplified diagram of the
thoracic structure
(right side view)

notum = thoracic tergum
T1 = prothorax
T2 = mesothorax
T3 = metathorax
A1 = propodeum

The thorax is made up of three segments called:

- *prothorax* (T1) – the first segment behind the head carrying one pair of legs
- *mesothorax* (T2) – the middle segment with one pair of legs, one pair of wings and a pair of spiracles
- *metathorax* (T3) – the rear segment with one pair of legs, one pair of wings and a pair of spiracles.

But then we have a complication in the form of the propodeum. This is a segment (A1) borrowed from the abdomen. Incorporating this extra segment into the thorax gives it a greater volume for the huge flight muscles.

The abdomen (properly now called the *gaster* because it has a segment missing) is made up of segments A2 to A10, but another complication arises here: segments A8, A9 and A10 are hidden inside A7 and so cannot be seen (although parts of A8 and A9 are visible in the drone). Segments A1 to A8 each have one pair of spiracles.

Each thoracic segment is composed of a tergum, a sternum and two pleura. The pleura are missing from the abdominal segments, so each one is made up of a tergum and a sternum only which overlap at the side of the insect. The propodeum, functionally part of the thorax but developmentally part of the abdomen, has only a tergum and a sternum.

Between the thorax and abdomen is a narrow constriction called the *petiole*. It is a narrow membranous bridge between A1 and A2 and is extremely important. Structures that are common to the abdomen and thorax, pass through it and it also enables the

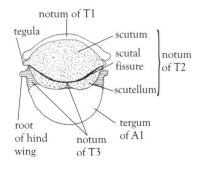

notum of T1
tegula
                    scutum
                    scutal
                    fissure   notum
                                 of T2
                    scutellum
root
of hind   tergum
wing   notum   of A1
        of T3

Simplified diagram of the
thoracic structure
(dorsal view)

abdomen to move very freely in relation to the thorax. Among other things, this allows the bee to bend its abdomen over when stinging.

NEW SKINS FOR OLD

As we have seen, the outer covering of an insect is of vital importance to it and its structure has enabled the insects to become, in many ways, the most successful group of animals. The skin's layered structure protects and gives rigidity to the insect, provides attachment for muscles, allows an enormous range of movement and restricts the loss of water from the insect's body.

The major disadvantage of a rigid outer covering is that it does not allow growth to take place on any scale. Because of this, during the early part of its life when it is growing very rapidly, the insect has to moult several times.

The honey bee is no exception. Its rate of growth is one of the fastest known and during the first four days as a larva, it moults on a daily basis. The fifth moult results in the formation of the pupa which remains inside the last larval skin for two to three days before finally shedding it. In this form, it is called the prepupa (or propupa). A sixth moult occurs just before the adult bee emerges, when it casts off its pupal skin.

These last two moults are not associated with growth but with the metamorphosis from larva to adult. In most insects, the process of moulting is fraught with danger because, apart from the fact that such a complex process is bound to go wrong in a proportion of cases, the insect is immobile for a time and is therefore very vulnerable to predators. The honey bee larva is a very cosseted individual and is protected from external predators within the colony.

Moulting and ecdysis

These two terms are often used to mean the same thing but, if we are being really fussy, they have different definitions. Moulting (sometimes called apolysis) is the separation of the old cuticle from the new one and precedes ecdysis, which is the emergence of the insect from the old cuticle.

The whole process is under the control of hormones (see Chapter 3) and is initiated by the hormone, ecdysone. It occurs when levels of juvenile hormone fall and those of ecdysone rise. The following sequence of events takes place:

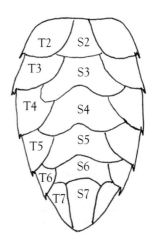

Ventral abdominal segmentation of the worker honey bee

T = tergum
S = sternum

a procuticle separated by fluid
   from epidermis
b moulting fluid produced by
   epidermal cells
c epidermis cells divide to produce
   many more

Moulting

*The first stage in the development
of a new cuticle*

- the cells of the epidermis become very active, dividing to give a lot more cells
- the cuticle separates from the epidermis
- moulting fluid exudes from the epidermal cells into the cavity formed
- the epicuticle of the new skin is formed by the epidermis
- enzymes in the moulting fluid are activated and dissolve the old endocuticle
- the digested endocuticle and fluid are absorbed
- the larva swallows air, causing an increase in pressure and the rupture of the old exocuticle.

A few important points emerge from this sequence. Moulting occurs fairly early on in the process. Ecdysis is the last in our list. It is essential that the new, impervious, waxy epicuticle is laid down before the enzymes in the moulting fluid are activated or the new cuticle would be digested as well as the old one. The process of digestion and reabsorption is an efficient way of conserving materials. At the end of the process, the procuticle is not differentiated into endocuticle and exocuticle and this state of affairs remains in the honey bee larva. Because of this, the cuticle of the larva is pale, thin and almost transparent. It becomes differentiated and sclerotised, and therefore dark and hard, only when the adult develops after the sixth moult.

Add-on extras

The exoskeleton is used to fashion appendages because it is hard and can be shaped for various jobs. Many of these will be considered in the next section but some, the sensillae, will be included in the section on the nervous system.

MOUTHPARTS

Special legs

Insects have appendages on their heads which are designed to obtain food. These are collectively called 'mouthparts' but we have to remember that insects are part of the enormous group of animals called the Arthropoda (jointed-limbed animals), so the mouthparts are really modified jointed limbs or legs arising from some of the segments which have been joined together to form the insect's head.

To bite or to suck – that is the question!

All insects have mouthparts based on the same basic plan but that plan is adapted, depending upon the type of diet which the insect has. Many insects chew pieces from leaves or other fairly solid food while others, including the honey bee, suck up liquid food. Some suck liquids (usually plant sap or blood) after piercing a leaf, stem or skin. Some are omnivores, eating anything. Others are strictly herbivores and others carnivores, but in each case we can decide what type of food the particular insect uses by looking at the structure of the mouthparts.

The general pattern

I am going to start with the basic mouthpart plan found in an insect such as a cockroach and then we shall try to understand the more complicated adaptations found in the honey bee. There are five structures making up the feeding apparatus of any insect.

1 *Labrum* (upper lip) – an extension of the face of the insect. It serves no purpose in biting the food but forms the front of a space called the *pre-oral cavity*. Its muscles allow it to move backwards and forwards and, to a limited degree, sideways.
2 *Mandibles* (principal jaws) – paired structures situated immediately behind the labrum. They are toughened and the inner edge is toothed. Their movement is from side-to-side (laterally) and they act just like teeth, biting and chewing when they come together. (Find yourself a fairly large caterpillar and, using a hand lens, watch it chew a leaf to see how the mandibles work.)
3 *Maxillae* (accessory jaws) – found immediately behind the mandibles. Each maxilla is divided into two main parts. Nearest the head (proximal) is the *cardo* (plural: cardines) and next to that the *stipes* (plural: stipites). Then there are extra bits all attached to the stipes: furthest from the head (distal) is the inner *lacinia* and outer *galea*. Finally, on the side of the stipes is a *palp*. I hope the diagrams make it clearer – you'll just have to learn the names! All the various bits of the maxilla have their own muscles so that they can be moved and, in an insect like the cockroach, the maxillae scrape food back into the cavity behind. The palp is a sensory structure used to test the quality of food.
4 *Labium* (lower lip) – with a similar structure to the maxillae but the two sides are joined in the middle. Of course, the parts all have different names, because otherwise life might be too easy!

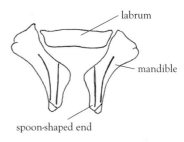

The mandibles and labrum of the worker honey bee

These are very similar to the basic biting insect pattern

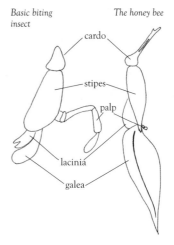

Maxilla of a generalised insect compared with a honey bee

The honey bee maxilla is very similar to the basic structure but the cardo and galea have been much elongated, the palp has been reduced and the lacinia has become a small pad

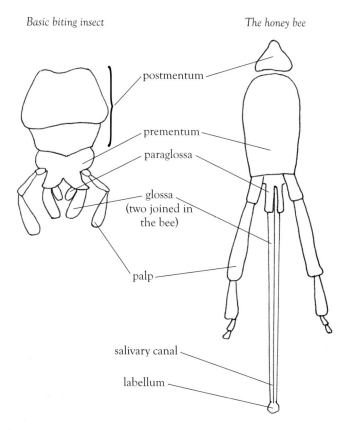

Basic biting insect   The honey bee

postmentum

prementum

paraglossa

glossa
(two joined in
the bee)

palp

salivary canal

labellum

The labium

*In the honey bee the postmentum is
reduced, the prementum is elongated
and the two glossae of the biting
insect are joined to form a single
structure called the glossa*

Below, I indicate which parts correspond to one another in the two structures:

- *postmentum* (subdivided into submentum and mentum) = cardines in the maxillae
- *prementum* = stipites in the maxillae
- *glossa* = lacinia in the maxilla
- *paraglossa* = galea in the maxilla
- *labial palps* correspond to the maxillary palps and also have a sensory function.

5   The *hypopharynx* – like a tongue situated between the two maxillae. It is mostly membranous with hairs on its upper side. It is hardened in places, particularly on the anterior surface where a tough, narrow bridge runs across it and then bends upwards to form two narrow arms which are connected to muscles coming from the front of the head. At either end of the 'bridge' on the hypopharynx are small toughened plates which connect to other muscles so that the whole structure can move backwards and forwards.

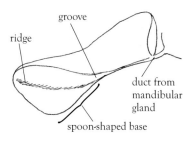

groove

ridge

duct from
mandibular
gland

spoon-shaped base

The worker mandible

(inner surface)

Important spaces

We have mentioned the pre-oral cavity which is the space within the mouthparts. It is closed by the labrum and the front part of the 'face' at the front and by the postmentum behind. It is not part of the inside of the insect so, technically, it is external. Part of this cavity has another name. It is called the cibarium and is the part of the pre-oral cavity at the top between the front of the head and the base of the hypopharynx. The food is received here from the mandibles and is then passed on to the true mouth which is at the innermost point of the cibarium. It does not seem very important in the biting insects but when we look at the honey bee, we shall see that it has a vital function.

HONEY BEE MOUTHPARTS

In the last section we looked at the structure of the mouthparts of an insect, such as a cockroach, which is more primitive than the honey bee. Now that we have understood all the big words, it is time to move on and look at the way in which the various parts have been modified in our bees. The modifications are necessary because the honey bee uses mainly liquid food and needs mouthparts which can suck up nectar and honey (and water).

We will start with the *labrum* and *mandibles* as they are almost unchanged. There is a small structure on the inside of the labrum, called the *epipharynx*. This is a soft flap. The mandibles of the honey bee are very important tools and are used for taking in pollen, shaping and chewing wax, fighting, grooming, dragging out debris from the nest, feeding brood, gathering and using propolis and to support the other mouthparts when they are in use. They are smoother and more spoon-like in shape than those of our typical insect but are still powerful structures.

The *maxillae* and *labium* are a different story. All the parts are still there but some of them have changed to produce a long sucking instrument, called the *proboscis*. Put simply, this is a long flexible tube surrounded by another tube. The central tube is called the *glossa* and is made from the two *glossae* of the labium, fused together. A deep groove runs along its length, forming a canal down which saliva can flow, and the whole structure ends in a rounded pad called the *labellum* (or sometimes the flabellum, just to confuse). The outer tube is made from four components – the two *galeae* (from the maxillae) at the front and the two *labial palps* at the back. The liquid food is drawn up this cavity. In this way, the maxillae and labium are modified to produce the sucking apparatus which the bee needs.

The part of the proboscis shown here is about 5 mm long. Part of it is obscured by the mandibles

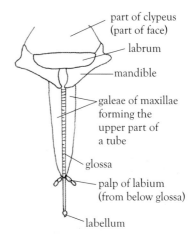

part of clypeus (part of face)

labrum

mandible

galeae of maxillae forming the upper part of a tube

glossa

palp of labium (from below glossa)

labellum

The mouthparts of a worker honey bee from the front

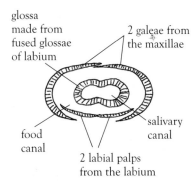

glossa made from fused glossae of labium

2 galeae from the maxillae

food canal

salivary canal

2 labial palps from the labium

Transverse section through the proboscis of the worker honey bee

The proboscis is a tube surrounded by another tube. Saliva passes down the salivary canal and nectar/water/honey is drawn up the food canal by the pump formed by the cibarium and the pharynx

Of the other parts, the cardines are long and slender and are joined together by a stiff rod called the *lorum*. Between the two cardines, the postmentum is also joined to the lorum. The prementum and stipites are the next to be connected and all are elongated. This collection of parts with long names acts as a hinge and, when the proboscis is not in use, the cardines swing the whole lot back, the stipites fold forward and the parts making up the proboscis fold back. The complete structure is in the shape of a letter 'z' and is stowed away in an inverted U-shaped space behind the head, called the *fossa*. When it wants to use the proboscis, the bee reverses this manoeuvre and swings it forward and up. The lacineae, which are reduced in size to small pads, join with the epipharynx to press against the upper end of the proboscis, creating an airtight seal, and the mandibles hold it in position.

If you are lost by now, have a break! Go and find yourself a recently-dead bee and have a good look at it with a powerful hand lens or a dissecting microscope. You will then be able to see the various parts and get a better idea of how they work.

The *cibarial pump* is the means by which liquid is drawn up the proboscis. Remember, the cibarium is the space at the top of the mouthparts between the front of the head and the base of the *hypopharynx*. The hypopharynx, as well as forming the floor of the cibarium, is fused to the sides of the prementum, so it is a vital structure in making the cibarium an enclosed space. When the bee feeds, powerful muscles pull on the walls of the cibarium, causing it to expand and so draw in fluid through the proboscis. The *pharynx*, which is behind the cibarium and a continuation of it, also has many muscles attached to it and this probably draws the liquid from the cibarium and passes it into the oesophagus. Beautifully designed and functional.

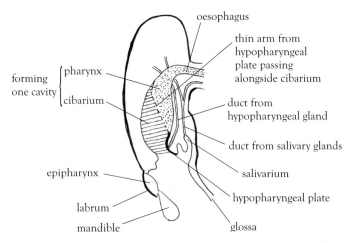

oesophagus

thin arm from hypopharyngeal plate passing alongside cibarium

forming one cavity

pharynx

cibarium

duct from hypopharyngeal gland

duct from salivary glands

salivarium

epipharynx

hypopharyngeal plate

labrum

mandible

glossa

Longitudinal section through the head to show the mouth cavities

(based on Dade, 1977)

A little complication

When a honey bee encounters solid food, such as sugar, the labellum comes into its own. Saliva pours down the glossal channel onto the food. The underside of the labellum, with its tough hairs, rubs the solid food and then the bee is able to suck up the resultant liquid. Easy!

ANTENNAE

The two antennae are attached to the front of the head. They are connected in a way which enables them to move in all directions. This is important because they carry many sense organs which tell the bee a great deal about its environment. The diagram shows how they are built and there is more about them in Chapter 3.

LEGS AND GADGETS

All insect legs are built to the same basic pattern and we will look at this first. There are six different parts, each one controlled by its own muscles and joined to the one(s) next to it by membranous structures, which allow it to move. As with most things biological, the names of the parts can be difficult to remember. I have devised a mnemonic to help you remember the order of the parts.

One complication which may confuse is the structure of the tarsus. In most insects, this is divided into a number (five in the

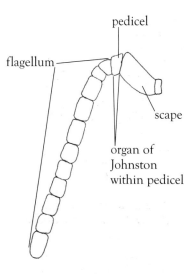

The antenna of the drone

The antennae of the honey bee contain an enormous number of sensilla making them vital structures in the bee's perception of its environment

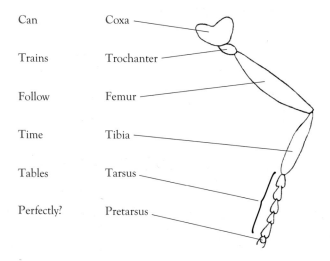

Can	Coxa
Trains	Trochanter
Follow	Femur
Time	Tibia
Tables	Tarsus
Perfectly?	Pretarsus

A mnemonic to help remember the parts of the leg

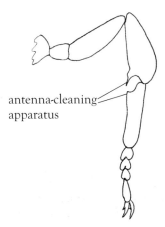

Worker – front leg

antenna-cleaning
apparatus

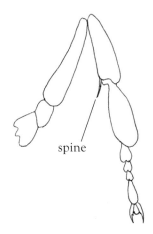

spine

Worker – middle leg

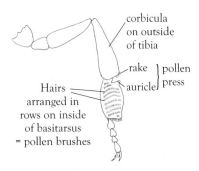

corbicula
on outside
of tibia

rake   } pollen
auricle } press

Hairs
arranged in
rows on inside
of basitarsus
= pollen brushes

Worker – hind leg

bee) of smaller sub-sections, called *tarsomeres*. 'Why aren't they separate sections?' I hear you ask. The answer is that they do not have individual muscles, as do all the other parts.

The other part which needs some description is the pretarsus, or foot, which usually consists of a pair of claws connected to a plate, attached to the last tarsomere, and a pad called the *arolium*.

The legs are hollow and the outer coverings are hard, with a covering of hairs. When they are used for walking at normal speed, the six legs function as two sets of tripods: the front and hind legs on one side and the middle leg on the other side are put on the surface together and then alternated with the other three. At very slow speeds, and sometimes at very fast ones, this system is modified. Different insects have different life-styles so that legs might be used for digging, swimming, running rapidly, jumping, making noises and so on, and for each of these functions there will be modifications.

The legs of the worker honey bee

Of course, the honey bee has complications – in your next life, study cockroaches! Although the legs of the honey bee follow the same general pattern, there are built-in gadgets to enable it to perform certain jobs. We will look at each part in turn and see where the problems arise.

- The coxa and trochanter are straightforward.
- The femur is slightly different. In the typical insect, it is the biggest, strongest part of the leg, but in the honey bee it is not.
- The tibia of the hind leg is wider and flatter than in the typical case. Its outer side is slightly concave and fringed with long, curved hairs. It is called the *corbicula*, or pollen basket, and is the structure in which the worker bee carries loads of pollen or propolis. In the foreleg near the distal end is a small, downward-pointing hard flap called the *fibula* which is part of the apparatus used for cleaning the antennae. The tibia of the middle leg has no special modification.
- The tarsus has its five tarsomeres but the first, nearest the body, is enlarged and rather flattened in all three legs. Naturally, it has yet another name and different authors give it different names! The name I prefer is the *basitarsus* because it is the basal (nearest the body) part of the tarsus, but it is sometimes called the metatarsus. This is a very important part of the worker bee's leg. In all three legs, it is covered on the inside by rows of short, stiff bristles. These

are used in the forelegs to clean the head and in the middle legs to clean the thorax, remove pollen from the forelegs and pass it on to the hind legs. In the hind legs, they are used for collecting all the pollen, which is then scraped into the joint between the tibia and basitarsus on the opposite side of the body so that it can be packed in the pollen basket. The basitarsus of the foreleg has a notch containing a comb at its base on its inner side and this is the antenna cleaner. The other four tarsomeres follow the basic pattern.

- The pretarsus fits the general description. The claws are used for gripping rough surfaces and when the bee has to walk on a smooth surface, it uses the arolium.

The foot has claws for rough surfaces and a suction pad (arolium) for smooth surfaces

USING THE GADGETS

It must be a great help to have inbuilt hairbrushes and combs together with containers to carry the food home, but these are some of the jobs that the honey bee's legs do and, in this section, we will look at the gadgets they carry and see how they work.

Cleaning the antennae

The antennae are very sensitive structures. They function as the bee's 'nose' and, as bees live in a world of scent, are very important to it. As with any sensitive structure, the antennae must be kept very clean and the bee therefore has a specialised antenna cleaner on each front leg. This is made up of two parts:

- a semicircular notch on the inside at the base (nearest the body) of the basitarsus, lined with stiff bristles forming a comb.
- a small hard flap called the *fibula* (in Latin 'fibula' means a clasp). This is attached to the inner edge of the distal (furthest from the body) end of the tibia. A small projection of the inside edge of the tibia overlaps it on the inside.

To clean the antenna, the bee moves its leg so that the antenna is trapped by the notch. The joint between the basitarsus and tibia is then flexed (bent) and this brings the fibula across the opening of the notch. It is held firm by the projection of the tibia and, as the antenna is drawn through, the pollen and dust are removed by the comb in the notch and the scraping action of the fibula. Queens and drones also have antennae cleaners and it is easy to see drones using them, often as they prepare to leave the hive entrance.

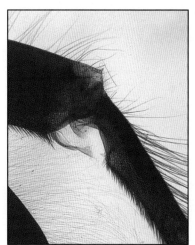

The antenna cleaner on the front leg of the worker honey bee

The inside surface of the hind leg with a pollen load in the corbicula

Pollen collection

As a honey bee visits flowers, pollen grains become entangled in the branched hairs which cover its whole body. Bees, of course, need pollen and they have a beautiful system for carrying it back home, but they do not need it all over them! All the legs are concerned with pollen cleaning and collection. The inside of the basitarsus of each leg is covered with horizontal rows of short bristly hairs which act like clothes brushes. The front pair clean the head and it is often possible to see a bee doing this (it reminds me of a rabbit washing its face and ears). The second pair clean the thorax. It is difficult for the bee to clean the very top of the second thoracic segment so pollen often remains there (after all you probably have difficulty scratching the middle of your back!). The third pair collect pollen from the abdomen and form part of the intricate pollen-harvesting equipment.

Transporting pollen

A bee may just remove pollen from its body, but it may also collect it in its pollen baskets or *corbiculae* and carry it back to the hive. The equipment for collecting and transporting pollen is made up of:

- *pollen brushes* on the inside of the basitarsus
- the *corbicula* on the outside of the tibia
- the *rastellum* (rake) which is a fringe of downwardly pointing stiff hairs on the inner side of the tibia
- the *auricle* which is the flattened hollow on the end of the basitarsus. It tilts upward and outward, is covered with small teeth and has a fringe of hairs on the outer edge.

Both the rastellum and auricle are part of the tibio-tarsal joint and this joint is called the *pollen press*.

- The pollen collected on the first two pairs of legs is passed to the pollen brushes on the hind legs. It has already been moistened with a small amount of nectar.
- The hind legs are rubbed together while the bee is in flight and the rastellum of one leg combs the pollen downwards from the pollen brushes of the opposite leg. It falls onto the auricle.
- The tibio-tarsal joint is flexed, bringing the auricle in contact with the tibia above. The hairs surrounding the auricle prevent the pollen falling out and it is pushed up onto the corbicula.

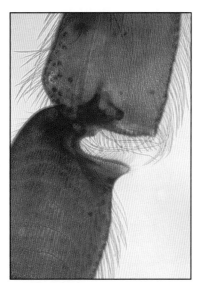

The pollen press on the hind leg of the worker honey bee

This action is repeated many times and the bee uses its middle legs to help form the pollen load. The single large hair in the centre of the corbicula is essential to forming the load. It is fascinating to watch a bee packing pollen as it hovers in front of a flower. Some bees are very efficient at this, others less so, but when the bee has adequate pollen loads on both legs it heads for home where it drops its loads into a cell. The loads dislodge very easily, often falling off in the hive before the bee can put them safely into a cell. The bee also uses its corbiculae to carry propolis but, when it gets back to the hive, it is unable to release these loads and other bees must chew these off using their mandibles.

WINGS AND FLIGHT

In our bid to understand the complexities of the bee world, we sometimes lose sight of the wonder. As you watch your bees leaving and returning to the hive, do you ever imagine what it would be like to walk out of the front door and soar into the air on gossamer wings? Sadly, though, facts and understanding usually have to replace imagination, so I am going to attempt to partially unravel the wonder of flight. It is perhaps worth mentioning that only three groups of animals have acquired the power of natural, sustained flight: insects, birds and bats. Of these, the birds and bats use adapted front limbs, but insects use specially constructed wings which develop as outgrowths of the cuticle, independently of the legs, thus leaving all six legs available for locomotion.

To understand the mechanics of flight, we must look at the structure of the thorax again (see page 4). There we can see that the thorax is made of three segments plus another one borrowed from the abdomen. Each segment is made of sclerotised plates, but they are not all simple. The tergum of each thoracic segment is usually called the *notum* and, in T2 (mesothorax), this is divided into an anterior part, called the *scutum*, and a posterior part, called the *scutellum*. The two parts are separated by a groove called the *sulcus* which, internally, is thickened into a ridge. The whole thorax is very heavily sclerotised and various plates are joined so that the whole forms a rigid box and it is difficult to tell which segment is which. This strong structure is able to withstand the stresses put on it by the huge muscles which control flight. The scutum of the mesothorax is divided into two parts by a trans-scutal fissure (a groove running from one side of the scutum to the other) which extends the full width of the notum, forming a hinge in the middle area and having membranes in the lateral part. This enables the thorax to change shape.

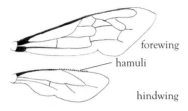

The wings of the worker honey bee

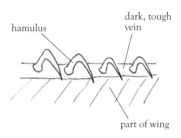

The hamuli

There are about 20 hamuli on the leading edge of each hindwing. They hook over a fold in the hind edge of each forewing

The wings

The honey bee has two pairs of wings; the front pair attached to the mesothorax (T2) and the hind pair attached to the metathorax (T3). Each wing is joined to the notum and supported by processes on the pleuron beneath it. Because of the way in which it articulates, it is capable of an up-and-down motion and a twisting motion when in flight and it can also be folded over the bee's back when it is not flying. The two pairs of wings are independent of one another when at rest but, when they are brought into the flying position, hooks (the *hamuli*) on the front edge of each hindwing hook into a fold on the rear edge of the front wing so that the two wings act as a single unit.

Flight

The basic up-and-down movement of the wings results from the contractions of large muscles in the thorax causing distortion of the box which we have described above. Because muscles can only pull, they occur in pairs which work in opposite directions and so are antagonistic. The thorax of the bee is occupied almost entirely by huge pairs of muscles which, because they do not act directly on the wings, are called *indirect flight muscles*.

The *dorsoventral muscles* are connected to the lateral parts of the scutum and to the lower wall of the appropriate thoracic segment. When they contract, the notum is pulled downwards and, because of the way in which the wings articulate, they move upwards. These muscles may also be called *elevator muscles* because they elevate the wings. Interestingly, there are dorsoventral muscles in the mesothorax (the biggest ones) and metathorax, so each pair of wings can be elevated by its own pair of muscles.

The *longitudinal muscles* are attached to the very front and the curved part of the mesoscutum. They run backwards and downwards to connections with the hind end of the mesothorax, which is actually situated inside the propodeum. When these muscles contract, they cause the mesothorax to become domed and the wings are pulled downwards. These muscles may also be called *depressor muscles*. There are no corresponding muscles in the metathorax, so both pairs of wings are depressed by the single pair of muscles.

There are other smaller muscles which assist with these movements but they are outside the scope of this book.

During flight, the wings follow a figure-of-eight pattern with the front margin of the forewing angled downwards on the downstroke to give lift. On the upstroke, it is angled upwards. Use your hand to work this out! Yet more muscles cause finer movements and these are known as *direct flight muscles* because they are attached to small sclerites at the base of the wing, so having a direct action on the articulation of the wing.

Of course, this is only a part of the story! Still more muscles are responsible for the extension of the wings prior to flight and the flexion of them when at rest. A bee does not always fly in a straight line; it may hover or perhaps even fly backwards. How does it do this? How does the bee cope with winds? I certainly cannot answer these questions but isn't it good to retain a little mystery and magic?

THE STING

Why doesn't everyone keep bees? After all, they take up very little space, use other people's land, do not need daily attention and produce a valuable, saleable product. That is more than can be said for most pets! They are somewhat lacking in the cuddly factor of course, you cannot take them for walks and there are a lot of strange people in this world who are not fascinated by insects and do not like 'creepy-crawlies' of any kind. But the one overriding snag, as far as most people are concerned, has to be the sting – that tiny structure at the rear end which assumes gigantic proportions in the minds of the general public (and many novice beekeepers). Small it may be, but the sting is a beautifully designed apparatus which allows the bee to defend its nest against predators and, since man, and particularly the beekeeping man (or woman), is the greatest predator of all, naturally (s)he suffers more than most.

What is the sting?

The abdomen proper (accurately called the gaster) of the bee appears to have six segments (A2–A7) but, in fact, has nine. The remaining three segments (A8, A9 and A10) are very much reduced and are inside segment A7. In many insects, including some other members of the Hymenoptera like the sawflies, ichneumons and their kin, these final segments are developed into a device for placing an egg accurately in crevices, leaves or wood – that is, an ovipositor – and this adaptation has been developed further in the wasps and bees so that the ovipositor has become a sting. It follows, then, that only females can have stings.

The parts of the sting

The cavity within segment A7 is called the *sting chamber* and the whole of the sting apparatus is enclosed within it (except when the sting is in use). The parts of the sting are:

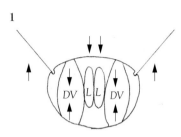

1

a dorsoventral muscles (DV) contract
b longitudinal muscles (L) relax
c roof of thorax pulled down
d wings raised

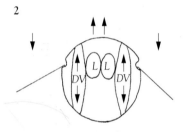

2

a longitudinal muscles contract
b dorsoventral muscles relax
c roof of thorax domed
d wings lowered

**Action of the indirect
flight muscles**

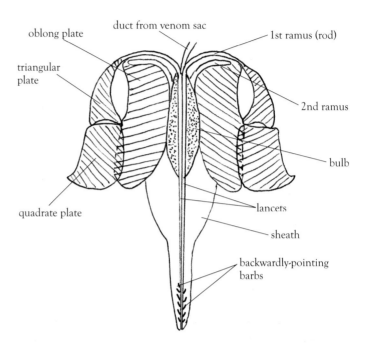

The worker sting

(ventral view)

- Three plates, *oblong*, *quadrate* and *triangular*, on each side.
- Several pairs of *muscles* whose actions result in movements of the sting as a whole and some of its individual parts.
- The *shaft* (the bit that goes into your finger), made up of three very fine and sharply pointed structures which zip together to leave a canal down the middle. These are the paired *lancets* and a single *stylet*. The stylet lies on the upper (dorsal) side of the lancets and its inner end is swollen into a larger structure called the *bulb*. This contains a pair of *umbrella valves* to push venom down into the shaft when it has been driven into the victim.
- The *venom sac* which holds the venom and empties into the bulb. The 'neck' between the venom sac and the bulb is held open by rigid rings of tissue.
- The *poison glands* which are long extensions of the venom sac. Their closed ends are thickened and lined with cells which secrete the venom.
- The *Dufour gland* which opens into the front of the sting chamber. It may lubricate the sting and do various other jobs but nobody is very sure.

See the diagram of the virgin queen's reproductive system (page 71) for the glands. In some books the poison gland is called the acid gland and the Dufour gland is called the alkaline gland.

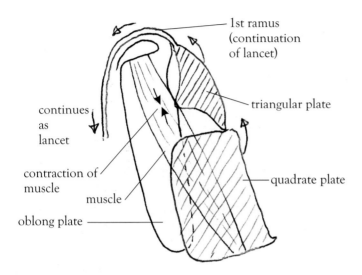

1st ramus (continuation of lancet)

triangular plate

continues as lancet

contraction of muscle

muscle

oblong plate

quadrate plate

Diagram showing the movements of the plates on one side of the sting

(arrows indicate direction of movement)

How does it work?

So, we have a reservoir containing venom, three pointy bits with a canal down the middle and numerous strangely-named structures associated with them. What do all these bits do when a bee stings?

Before the sting is used, the bee curves its abdomen downwards. This is achieved by the muscles connecting the abdominal sclerites. One set on the lower (ventral) side contracts, so pulling the sclerites together and shortening this section. Another different set on the upper (dorsal) side contracts so that these plates are extended. The result is a bending downwards of the abdomen. Some muscles connected to the sting itself also contract so that the whole sting is swung downwards. At the moment of entry, the sting shaft makes an angle of about 90° with the surface upon which the bee is standing. The combined forces of the legs and the muscles of the abdomen push on the sting and the three pairs of plates come into play.

- The two oblong plates, which lie either side of the bulb, are fixed and *do not move*.
- Each oblong plate articulates (joins at a moveable joint) with the triangular plate which, in its turn, articulates with the quadrate plate.
- A muscle is attached at the front end of the oblong plate and the rear end of the quadrate plate. When this muscle contracts, the quadrate plate is pulled forwards.
- The triangular plate is pushed at its corner and swings on its joint with the oblong plate.
- The top corner of the triangular plate is continued as a long

curved rod (called a ramus) which is continuous with the lancet on that side of the sting. So, as the triangular plate swings forwards, the lancet is pushed downwards into the victim.

- A second muscle attached to the rear of the oblong plate and the front of the quadrate plate contracts to reverse the process and attempts to pull the plates back into their original position, ready for the next thrust.
- The two sides of the apparatus work alternately so that each lancet is driven down and, because of its backward-pointing barbs, cannot be withdrawn and therefore digs further in.

But what about the rest of the apparatus? You will be pleased to hear that it is quite simple. The poison is produced in the swollen parts of the poison gland. It drains down into the venom sac, which is merely a reservoir, and from here it drains into the bulb of the sting. Within the bulb of the sting are two valves called *umbrella valves*. Each of these is connected to a lancet. As the lancet is driven down by the action of its plates, the umbrella valve, which is a cone of soft tissue, is pulled down with it. This causes the valve to expand and force venom down the narrow tube made by the fastening together of the lancets and stylet. The other lancet then moves downwards with the same effect on the other side. At the tip of the sting shaft, the venom escapes through a small gap at the tips of the lancets. More venom pours from the venom sac into the bulb.

A sacrifice

When a bee stings an enemy with a tough outer covering, such as us, the sting shaft digs its way in until the bee cannot withdraw it. Some of the structures in the sting chamber are only weakly held and, as the poor bee tries to withdraw its sting to fly away, the whole sting apparatus is torn out together with the last nerve ganglion, the quadrate plates, the small segment carrying the anus and part of the digestive system. Such an injured bee dies in a few days and, of course, is not able to sting again. The advantage of this to the colony as a whole is that a greater quantity of venom is delivered as it carries on passing into the victim from the detached sting. The deaths of a few individuals from the colony are insignificant in the grand scale of things.

A potent poison

Honey bee venom is pretty strong stuff. It is also complex, containing a large number of different chemicals. Some of these interact with each other and may be synergistic (two substances working together to increase the overall effect). We will look at a few of the main ingredients and their effects on vertebrates, including us.

A worker honey bee

- *Melittin* is a protein-type substance and makes up 50% of the dry weight of the venom constituents. It causes the rupture of blood and mast cells and depresses blood pressure and respiration (mast cells release histamine and heparin when they are ruptured).
- *Phospholipase A* is an enzyme which also causes breakdown of cells, and pain, and is synergistic with melittin.
- *Hyaluronidase* is an enzyme which attacks the 'cement' holding cells together, so allowing the other nasties to penetrate further. It is found in snake venom, too!

I could go on, but the names are long and I can imagine your eyes glazing over! Suffice it to say that there are several different effects of venom on the system and that, although most beekeepers develop immunity to bee venom, this can break down at any time for no apparent reason, leading to severe allergic reactions. Interesting as they are then, stings are best avoided whenever possible!

THE EXTERNAL DIFFERENCES BETWEEN WORKER, QUEEN AND DRONE

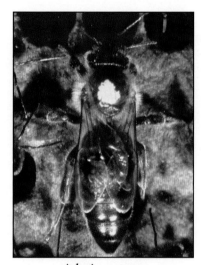

A laying queen

We have considered the structure of the outer covering of the bee and the specialist tools that are made from it and, in later chapters, we will look at function and behaviour. However, I want to pause for a short while to summarise the external differences between the three types of honey bee. It is quite possible to produce a list of these differences and try to remember them but that is difficult and I suggest we use the functional approach.

A basic design

There are more similarities than differences between the three types of bee. They are all built of three parts – head, thorax and abdomen. On the head are mouthparts, made up of mandibles and a proboscis, one pair of compound eyes, three ocelli and one

A drone

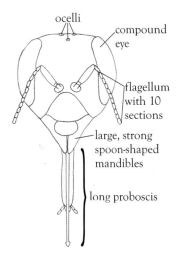

Head of a worker

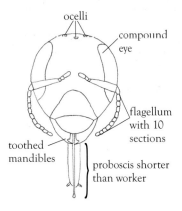

Head of a queen

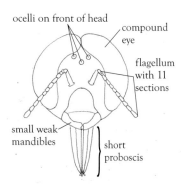

Head of a drone

pair of antennae. The thorax is made up of three thoracic segments (T1–T3) plus the propodeal segment (A1) borrowed from the abdomen. T2 and T3 each carry one pair of legs and one pair of wings and T1 carries another pair of legs. The first pair of legs incorporates a device for cleaning the antennae. The gaster (abdomen minus propodeum) is made up of nine segments (A2–A10). There are ten pairs of spiracles, one pair on each segment from T2 to A8. The whole structure is covered by a hard outer covering which is built into plates and protects the insect as well as providing an attachment for muscles.

Now the differences!

Jills of all trades – the workers

Workers have to do all the jobs in the nest as well as defending it from attack and doing the shopping, so they are adapted for this role by having tools of various kinds. On their heads, their *compound eyes* have up to 6900 ommatidia each. The *proboscis* is fairly long (5.5–7.0 mm) to enable the bee to reach into flowers for nectar (it is also used in nectar processing) and the *mandibles* are strong, spoon-shaped, ridged structures used for eating pollen, manipulating and shaping wax, scraping propolis, feeding brood, grooming, fighting and feeding the queen – almost the original multi-purpose tool. To carry the solid shopping (pollen and propolis) back to the nest, each worker bee has its *pollen baskets* on the modified tibiae of its hind legs. To help in collection of pollen and the loading of the baskets, the basitarsi and the tibio-tarsal joint are also modified.

That leaves us with the abdomen. The four pairs of *wax glands* are part of the epidermis (A4–A7) and found on the sterna. They produce the wax needed to build the comb which makes up the whole nest. The *Nasonov gland* is developed from the epidermis on the front of the tergum of A7 and its canal is visible externally when exposed by the bee. Finally, the worker bee has a straight, barbed *sting*.

The egg-laying machine

The queen spends most of her time inside the nest just laying eggs, but she does have to fly, both to mate in the early part of her life and when she leaves with a swarm later on. She also has to establish herself, at the beginning of her life, as the sole queen in the colony.

The most obvious difference between her and her workers is her *size*. The *large abdomen* is necessary to accommodate the huge ovaries. She is larger all over but is somewhat lacking in other ways. Her compound eyes have *fewer ommatidia* (about 4000 in each eye) and her antennae, although they have the same number of parts as those of the worker, carry *fewer sense organs*. She does not forage and is fed throughout her life, so her *proboscis is shorter*, but her *mandibles*, used only for tearing down queen cells, are toothed and quite sturdy. She has no *pollen baskets* or pollen-collecting apparatus, neither does she have *wax glands* or a *Nasonov gland*. She does have a *sting* but it is curved, with tiny barbs, and is usually used only to kill other queens.

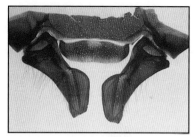

Worker mandibles are spoon-shaped

The flying gamete

The drone is adapted to perform one function – to mate with a queen. To that end, he is *bigger* than the worker. His *thorax is bigger* to accommodate the huge flight muscles that he needs to power *broader wings*, carry a *heavier body*, spend a great deal of time flying to drone congregation areas and chase queens. His *abdomen is larger* because, in the act of mating, his reproductive system turns inside out and that needs powerful pressure from abdominal muscles. Parts of two more abdominal segments are also visible. The tergum of segment A8 and the sternum of segment A9 are visible, while in the worker and queen these two segments, as well as segment A10, are all concealed within A7.

The drone's sensory system needs to be well developed, so his *antennae* each have an *extra section* in the flagellum and carry many *more sensilla* than do those of the worker (about ten times as many). His *compound eyes* contain up to 8600 ommatidia each and take up so much room that the *three ocelli* are pushed to the front of his face, rather than being on the top of the head as in the worker and queen. The structures which he lacks, or possesses in simplified form, are related to the fact that he does not do anything! The end of his *abdomen* is *blunt*. This is because, as a male, he has *no sting* (a female attribute which has developed from the egg-laying apparatus). He still needs food, but he does not spend his life probing flowers and maximising his nectar production, so his *proboscis is short*. His *mandibles* are small and he does not co-ordinate them very well and he has *no pollen baskets, wax glands* or *Nasonov gland*.

Queen mandibles are strong and toothed

Two sexes and two castes

I have tried to summarise the external differences between the two female castes, queen and worker, and the male sex in honey bees. There are also internal differences, but these are described

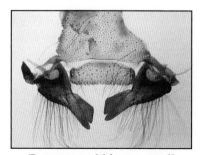

Drone mandibles are small and not well co-ordinated

elsewhere in this book and are fairly obvious. It is difficult to remember them all in the abstract, particularly for those of us for whom youth is a distant memory, but structure can always be related to function.

2 INTERNAL WORKINGS

THE DIGESTIVE SYSTEM

The digestive system of any animal has four distinct functions:

- *ingestion* – taking in food
- *digestion* – breaking the food down chemically to its simplest, soluble components
- *absorption* – passing those components through its wall to the blood
- *defecation* – removing any indigestible material from the body.

The system in the honey bee is complicated by its further function as a transport system for nectar and water.

A tube in three parts

The system is simply a tube which connects the front opening (the mouth) with the rear opening (the anus). In the embryo, before the egg hatches, it develops as three parts:

- *stomodeum* (foregut) – grows inwards from the front of the embryo
- *proctodeum* (hindgut) – grows inwards from the rear of the embryo
- *mesenteron* (midgut) – forms as a structure surrounding the yolk of the egg between the stomodeum and proctodeum.

When the larva hatches from its egg, the foregut and midgut have already fused to form a continuous tube but the join between midgut and hindgut is not completed until the larva is fully grown.

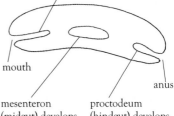

stomodeum (foregut) develops into cibarium, pharynx, oesophagus, crop and proventriculus

mouth

anus

mesenteron (midgut) develops into ventriculus

proctodeum (hindgut) develops into small intestine and rectum

The development of the digestive system in the embryo

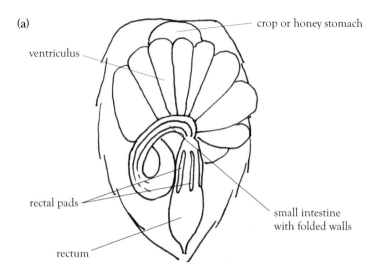

(a)

crop or honey stomach

ventriculus

rectal pads

small intestine with folded walls

rectum

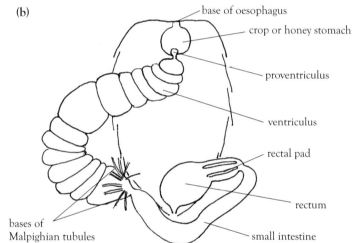

(b)

base of oesophagus

crop or honey stomach

proventriculus

ventriculus

rectal pad

rectum

bases of Malpighian tubules

small intestine

Dorsal view of the digestive system (alimentary canal) of a worker honey bee (all the Malpighian tubules have been removed)

(a) in situ

(b) displayed outside the abdomen

If we look at the different parts of the gut in the adult honey bee we can briefly describe the structure and function of each.

The *cibarium* and *pharynx* together (see diagram on page 10) form a cavity which can loosely be called a mouth. The walls of the cibarium are surrounded by muscles which can cause the area to expand and contract, so setting up a suction which draws liquids into the cavity. The pharynx is also surrounded by muscles which push the food towards the oesophagus. Two pairs of glands empty into the cibarium. These are:

- the *postcerebral glands* situated behind the brain (see diagrams opposite)
- the *thoracic glands* found in the thorax.

These glands are collectively called *labial glands* (because they develop originally from the part of the embryo forming the labium) or *salivary glands* (because their secretion empties into the mouthparts and contains digestive enzymes). They produce a liquid passing from the glands into tubes which fuse to give one common duct passing under the pharynx and opening into the base of the labium. The liquid then passes down the tube in the proboscis and is mixed with the incoming food. The saliva contains invertase which begins the breakdown of sucrose. Its other function is to lubricate dry foods. This is particularly important when a bee is confronted by crystallized stores.

The pharynx leads to the next part.

The *oesophagus* is the tube which carries the food down through the thorax and into the abdomen. The walls are surrounded by muscles. The fibres of the inner layer of muscles run longitudinally; those of the outer layer are circular. This is a common arrangement in digestive tubes and contractions of the muscles push the food along in waves. This type of movement is called *peristalsis*.

The *crop* (honey stomach) is the reservoir for the transport of nectar or water and, structurally, is just the lower, enlarged, part of the oesophagus which is capable of stretching to carry a heavy load (average 40 mg).

The *proventriculus* is a one-way valve controlling the flow of materials from the crop to the rest of the gut. When it is closed it prevents nectar or water leaving the crop and it has flaps and hairs which filter out the pollen grains in the nectar.

All the structures described so far constitute the foregut.

The *ventriculus* is the midgut and is sometimes called the true stomach because it is here that most digestion takes place. The tube is widened and lined by epithelium (epithelium is a general term to describe a sheet or tube of cells which stick firmly together with little between them and usually form linings). Outside the epithelium are two layers of muscle but beware, this time the circular ones are on the inside and the longitudinal ones are on the outside – just to keep you on your toes.

Enzymes and a *gelatinous envelope* are found in the ventriculus. Epithelial cells produce and release the digestive enzymes which break down the proteins, fats and complex sugars in the food into their simpler, constituent parts which can be absorbed through the wall of the gut and carried in solution in the haemolymph. The food is not in direct contact with the walls of the ventriculus but is surrounded by the *peritrophic membrane* made of a jelly-like material continuously produced along the whole length of the ventriculus by the epithelium. It forms an envelope around the food and probably protects the delicate walls of the ventriculus from abrasion by structures such as spiny pollen grains. The

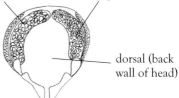

postcerebral (salivary) glands

dorsal (back wall of head)

Postcerebral glands

The thoracic glands in the ventral part of the thorax are similar

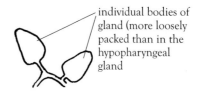

individual bodies of gland (more loosely packed than in the hypopharyngeal gland

Part of the postcerebral gland

Compare with the acini of the hypopharyngeal gland on page 40

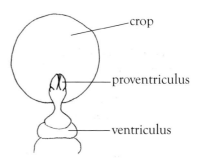

crop

proventriculus

ventriculus

The proventriculus projects into the crop

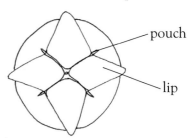

pouch

lip

Surface view of the proventriculus from the crop, with lips closed

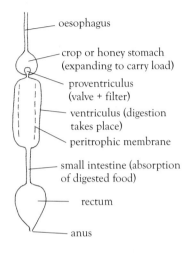

- oesophagus
- crop or honey stomach (expanding to carry load)
- proventriculus (valve + filter)
- ventriculus (digestion takes place)
- peritrophic membrane
- small intestine (absorption of digested food)
- rectum
- anus

Simple diagram to show the main parts of the digestive system

membrane allows enzymes and the soluble products of digestion to pass through it.

The rest of the structures make up the hindgut.

The *small intestine* is a long, much narrower tube, again lined with epithelium but with only one surrounding layer of circular muscle. The job of this part of the gut is to pass the products of digestion into the haemolymph which surrounds it, so the total surface area is increased by infolding of the walls. At the beginning of the small intestine (the area called the pylorus) are the openings of the Malpighian tubules which are part of the excretory system and do not concern us here.

The *rectum* is the part of the tube where the faeces accumulate. In cold winter weather it can expand enormously to store the waste until the bee can leave the hive and deposit it on the neighbour's clean car. In higher animals, the rectum absorbs water (and other useful substances) from the faeces. This is very important in land animals generally and also happens in the bee.

The *anus* is the opening to the outside. It is situated on the proctiger, the posh name for the 10th abdominal segment, which is reduced and hidden away inside the other segments as part of the sting chamber.

FAT BODIES

For some of us, fat bodies are a sensitive issue associated with over-indulgence, tightening waist bands and dieting! But for insects they are a different matter altogether and often a matter of life and death.

Although the vast majority of insects have a fat body, the term itself may be misleading because it is not a discrete structure, like the brain or an ovary, but rather a collection of cells forming loose aggregations in several places within the insect body. Neither are these cell masses static once they have formed but they are constantly changing. The function of the larval fat body is to build up food reserves during the period of larval feeding and then to contribute these reserves to the rebuilding of the adult structures during the pupal stage. It is the fuel for metamorphosis. The adult fat body also has an important function in relation to overwintering. In some other insects, such as queen bumblebees, the reserves of food in the fat body enable the insect to survive the winter without food.

Structure of the fat body

There are three kinds of cell within the fat body, each with quite different functions:

- *Trophocytes* are fat cells found throughout larval, pupal and adult life. These form the major part of the fat body.
- *Oenocytes* are found throughout larval, pupal and adult life.
- *Urate cells* are found only in the larva and pupa.

Development of the fat cells

- *Very young larva* – there are a few small fat cells containing oil globules.
- *Growing larva* – the fat cells increase in number and grow in size.
- *Mature larva* – the body cavity around the essential organs is filled with fat cells containing quantities of oil globules. The cells also contain large amounts of glycogen. This is a complex carbohydrate which can be rapidly broken down to glucose when needed. It is found only in animals and is sometimes called 'animal starch'. The fat body gives the larva its white appearance as it presses against the transparent skin.
- *Prepupa* – the fat cells float freely in the haemolymph. As well as the fat globules and the glycogen, granules of protein increase in the cells. This protein is mainly albumins which contain a mixture of a large number of different amino acids.
- *Early pupa* – the fat cells start to disintegrate, releasing their contents of oil, very large numbers of protein granules and carbohydrate into the haemolymph.
- *Late pupa* – during pupal life, the fat cells continue to disintegrate, releasing their contents. Towards the end of this period the protein granules will have disappeared and virtually all the fat cells will have disintegrated.
- *Adult worker* – new fat cells are formed, apparently from the few larval ones that remain.

Fat cells in the adult worker

These are few in number in a newly emerged bee but in an older one, the fat body forms thin sheets of cells, particularly in the dorsal and ventral sinuses and along the side walls of the abdomen. The fat and protein content of the cells varies with the time of year and age of the worker:

- *Young summer workers* – fat cells contain many fat globules and little protein.

- *Older summer workers* – protein granules accumulate in the fat cells.
- *Winter workers* – protein granules are very plentiful but there is only a small amount of fat.

The protein content of the cells appears to be related to brood food production. When bees are not producing brood food, protein accumulates in the fat cells. When they start producing brood food, the protein content of the cells diminishes, presumably being used up by the brood food glands.

Oenocytes

These cells are distributed throughout the fat body. The larval oenocytes are destroyed and new ones formed in the adult. They are found in almost all insects and are involved in the production of substances used for building the new cuticle. In the adult honey bee, they are found in high concentrations over the wax glands and reach their maximum size when the wax glands are at their peak of production. Isotope-labelled substances have been shown to pass from the oenocytes into the wax. The cells are larger in the queen and play a part in the formation of the egg yolk.

Urate cells

These cells, which are dispersed throughout the fat body in the larva and pupa, contain crystals of uric acid. They therefore act as storage reservoirs for nitrogenous waste in both larva and pupa. Once the Malpighian tubules become functional in the adult, the urate cells break down and disappear.

THE CIRCULATORY SYSTEM

Any complicated animal, like a honey bee needs a system for circulating fluid and materials within its body. Why?

- Cells need to be bathed by a fluid to survive and function.
- All living cells need a supply of food as a fuel to produce energy and as raw material for manufacture of other substances.
- Cells need a constant supply of oxygen in solution.
- Other materials, such as hormones, must be able to reach their 'target' areas.

- Waste, which is produced as a result of the activity of living cells, must be removed from them, or they will be poisoned by it.

In the bee, haemolymph is the fluid. In the first part of this section, we look at its circulation around the bee's body.

An open system

Most of us are reasonably knowledgeable about the heart and circulation of blood within the human body, but ours is a 'closed' system where the main circulation of blood is confined to tubes, whereas in the honey bee we have an 'open' circulatory system which is simpler. The organs in the head, thorax and abdomen are suspended in cavities and these spaces are filled with haemolymph. The honey bee can also truthfully be said to have hollow legs!

Now, that is fine, but we are discussing a transport system and movement is an essential part of it, so there are various structures which help the fluid go round the bee's body.

Ventral and dorsal diaphragms

This can be a difficult concept to grasp. Think of a fluid-filled shoebox (the bee's abdomen) with tiny rigid projections along its length, top and bottom. Then imagine two very thin sheets of material along the length of the box, one near the top (dorsal) and one near the bottom (ventral), connected at intervals to the projections but with the remainder open. (It's rather like a sheet pegged horizontally between two clothes lines.) These sheets are the two diaphragms and, whereas the dorsal one is restricted to the abdomen, the ventral one extends into the thorax. Our box is now divided up into three, interconnecting, cavities.

Now, if undulations are set up in the sheets in a rhythmic fashion, the fluid will move along in the direction of the undulations in the bottom cavity and the top cavity, and in the middle cavity it will swirl about. The diaphragms (sheets) contain muscle fibres which contract in sequence, so setting up the undulations.

The fluid in the cavity beneath the ventral diaphragm, the *ventral sinus* (a sinus is a space), moves from front to back and that in the *dorsal sinus* above the dorsal diaphragm moves from back to front. As the fluid moves, some of it surges through the spaces connecting the three cavities, into the central cavity.

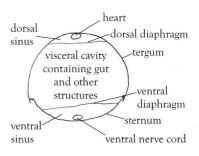

Transverse section through the middle part of the abdomen to show body cavities

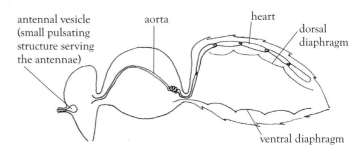

Lateral (side) view of the main parts of the circulatory system

(redrawn from Dade, 1977)

The heart, aorta and other blood vessels

The function of the heart is to propel haemolymph forward towards the head. It hangs below the dorsal wall, in the dorsal sinus, and is connected by fibres both to the body wall above and to the dorsal diaphragm below. It is a tube, closed at the back end, with five pairs of openings along its length called *ostia* (singular *ostium*). These effectively divide it up into a number of sections and allow the haemolymph to flow into the heart.

The walls of the heart are made of muscle. As the muscles contract, they squeeze the haemolymph forward and into the *aorta*. The ostia have flaps which close the openings as this happens. The muscles then relax, the ostia open, and more haemolymph flows in to fill up the cavity.

The aorta is a narrow tubular extension of the front end of the heart which passes through the petiole (waist), crosses the thorax and ends with an opening just behind the brain. A small structure between the bases of the antennae acts in a way similar to the heart. When it relaxes, haemolymph flows into it through an opening at the back. It then squeezes the fluid through two vessels which go into the antennae. The interesting thing is that the walls of this small beating structure do not contain muscle. It is thin-walled and attached to the muscles of the pharynx which are the ones which cause it to contract.

There you have it then. A simple system, with various structures which help the haemolymph to move from front-to-back and bottom-to-top of the bee. It is not as efficient as ours but still serves the bee well enough and has adaptations to keep the very important structures in the head well supplied with life-giving haemolymph.

Now we have to look more closely at the haemolymph.

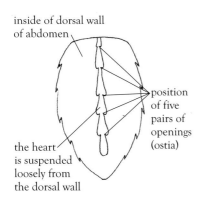

The heart as seen from a ventral dissection

Structure of the haemolymph

There are two parts to the haemolymph:

- *Plasma* is a watery liquid carrying a number of substances dissolved in it. It is colourless. (Perhaps we wouldn't be so cavalier about squashing bees if they spurted bright red blood!) The dissolved substances include salts, amino acids, proteins, carbohydrates, uric acid, lipids, fatty acids and many organic compounds which arise as a product of the activities of the bee's cells. Nothing surprising here since the main function of the plasma is as a transport system. The amounts of the various substances in the plasma vary with time and with the condition of the insect as well as changing at different stages in its life.

- *Haemocytes* are simply cells suspended in the plasma. Several kinds have been described by various authors but they are all similar – colourless and with nuclei. There is confusion over the number of types and it is possible that the same cell may have a different appearance at different times – all just designed to confuse!

Of more interest to us are the functions.

Functions of the haemolymph

1 *Transport*. This has been mentioned already. All the food needed by the cells must be carried to them from the gut and waste materials produced as a result of the cells' activity (metabolism) must be carried away to be excreted. Hormones must be taken from their point of production to the organs upon which they act. Although haemolymph is not as important in the respiration of an insect as it is in higher animals, oxygen and carbon dioxide do dissolve in the plasma. Some of the oxygen is used by the haemocytes and some is available to those cells not in direct contact with the tracheoles. Similarly, carbon dioxide is removed from the cells in some instances.

2 *Mechanical support*. It fills all the cavities of the bee's body, giving support and bathing all the living cells with fluid, which is essential for their life and activity. (Support is a more obvious function in the larva which is soft skinned – if there was no fluid inside, the larva would deflate like a punctured balloon!)

Changes in the fluid pressure, which are caused by muscular activity, result in the eversion of the penis during mating.

3 *Control of the water content of the cells*. All living cells need to have a stable environment in which to work and this is maintained as they are bathed with the haemolymph. Because of the concentrations of dissolved substances in the plasma, the water content of the cell is maintained and not allowed to fluctuate wildly. Where water is needed by a cell, it can obtain it from the surrounding haemolymph.

4 *Metabolism*. Chemical reactions take place in the haemolymph. Chemicals are broken down into simpler ones, particularly in relation to energy production. Many of the proteins in the plasma are enzymes which are essential for these reactions.

5 *Phagocytosis*. This is the fancy word for the action of some of the haemocytes in surrounding and destroying certain bacteria and parasites which enter the bee's body. Many of the haemocytes are involved in this activity and they may then be called phagocytes.

6 *Wound healing*. Damaged tissue is removed by the phagocytes so that new tissue can replace it. Other haemocytes form a network to plug any hole in the epidermis until this can be properly repaired.

An analogy

If we liken the body of the bee to a very complex factory then we can imagine that the various systems and organs are departments in that factory, each responsible for a particular part of its function. The circulatory system is the collection of all the methods by which raw materials reach all the departments, products are exchanged between departments and end products are removed. It removes the rubbish to a central point, from where it is removed from the factory, and includes an internal messenger system to kick-start or encourage particular areas of production. Finally, it is a medical and security system, providing the first-aiders for any accident or injury and the security staff to remove intruders. There our analogy must end because, luckily for the bee, the blood system does not take part in long, unnecessary meetings, go on strike or even take meal breaks. It is self-maintained and only stops when the whole organism does.

THE RESPIRATORY SYSTEM

We always need a supply of air. Without it we die very quickly and our bees are just the same. The part of the air that is so vital to us all is oxygen and all animals have to have some method for getting oxygen to their cells. Why is oxygen so necessary? It is needed to combine with the food in the cells to release the energy which was stored in that food. This chemical process, taking place in all living cells, is oxidation and the end result of the oxidation of food is the release of energy and the production of the waste products, carbon dioxide and water. Biologists call these chemical changes that go on inside cells *cellular* (or *tissue*) *respiration*. We are interested in how the oxygen gets to the cells and how the carbon dioxide is removed from them and this is called *breathing* or *respiration*.

Openings, tubes and a surface

Air is all around us, so to get it into the body all you need is an opening and a tube or tubes. Simple! But then the air needs to be carried to the cells – all the cells – and the oxygen has to pass from the tubes into the cells, which means a very thin surface through which it can move. Different animals have solved the problem in different ways and insects have their own (almost) unique type of respiratory system, called the tracheal system. Put simply, this is made up of a number of openings which lead into tubes. The tubes divide and divide until they are very numerous and very small, spreading throughout the body of the insect and carrying the air to all the living cells. The openings are called *spiracles*, the large tubes are called *tracheae*, the smaller tubes are called *tracheoles* and the total surface of all the tube endings, through which the oxygen and carbon dioxide move to and from the cells, is called the *respiratory surface*. This respiratory surface must be moist so that the gases can diffuse through it and, in order to fulfil this requirement, the ends of the tracheoles contain fluid.

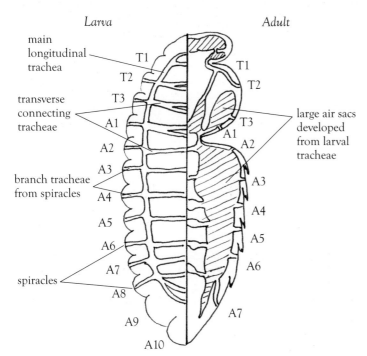

Larva   *Adult*

main longitudinal trachea

transverse connecting tracheae

branch tracheae from spiracles

spiracles

large air sacs developed from larval tracheae

T1 T2 T3 A1 A2 A3 A4 A5 A6 A7 A8 A9 A10

T1 T2 T3 A1 A2 A3 A4 A5 A6 A7

The larval and adult respiratory systems
(based on Dade, 1977)

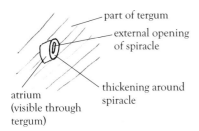

Surface view

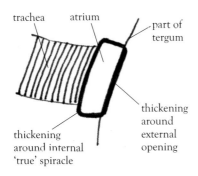

Lateral view

Abdominal spiracle

(drawn from A4 of a virgin queen)

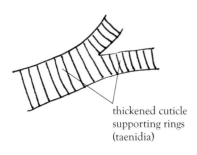

Small section of trachea

Understanding the structures

The spiracles

There are 10 pairs of spiracles. They are found on each of the segments from T2 to A8. They are not just simple holes because one of the problems of being a land-living animal is that water must be conserved in the body. If the spiracles were just open to the atmosphere, too much water would be lost from them and the insect would tend to dehydrate. So, spiracles are usually equipped with valves which allow them to be closed at times. When we look at the honey bee, we find that each of the spiracles on T2 has a 'lid' which can be pulled shut over the hole, but it can never be closed really firmly (see diagram on page 4). The opening is also surrounded by hairs. The spiracles on T3 seem to have no valve at all and are very small. The abdominal spiracles all have an entrance called an *atrium*, like a small hallway, between the surface of the cuticle and the valve. Tiny muscles control the valve. The two spiracles on the propodeum (A1) are the largest of all and the rest of the abdominal spiracles, although smaller than this pair, have a similar structure.

The tracheae

The *tracheae* are the tubes leading from the spiracles. They join together in the body of the bee to give two *lateral tracheae* running down the sides of the insect and these branch off into dorsal and ventral tracheae. The structure of the tracheae is interesting because they are lined with cuticle which is continuous with that covering the body. (It follows then, that at each larval and pupal moult, the lining of the tracheae is shed.) Within this cuticular lining are thickenings made of chitin. They look, under the microscope, like coiled springs wrapped round each tube and their function is to keep the tracheae open at all times so that, even when the air pressure inside them drops, they do not collapse. Each single turn of the spiral is called a *taenidium*.

The *tracheoles* do not normally have taenidia, although they may have some fairly disorganised sign of thickening, and their linings are not shed at moulting. Each tracheole has a blind ending and there seems some disagreement among authors whether the ends can go into cells or not. Certainly they penetrate between cells and may 'indent' cells, particularly those making up muscle tissue which needs a great deal of oxygen. At the end of each tracheole there is a small amount of fluid in which the oxygen and carbon dioxide dissolve so that they can diffuse through the very thin lining of the tracheole and the cell wall of the surrounding cells.

Air sacs

When you look at the diagram, you will see that there are some very prominent structures which do not fit into the description so far and which I have not mentioned. There are always complications. You would get bored otherwise!

Air sacs are simply tracheae with no taenidia in their walls. This means that they have thin walls, allowing them to expand or collapse like balloons. Most of the tracheae in the bee are modified in this way and they do look quite confusing but remember the basic pattern and then you can make sense of them. The air sacs are present in the head, thorax and abdomen.

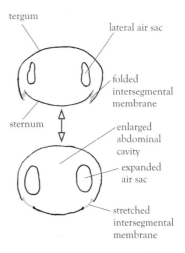

Respiratory movements

Similar movements act longitudinally increasing the length of the abdomen

Ventilation of the respiratory system

This sounds very grand but it really just describes the way in which fresh air is drawn into the system and 'stale' air pushed out again.

If you look carefully at a live honey bee you will see that its abdomen moves rhythmically. These are *respiratory movements*. The sternum and tergum of each abdominal segment can move away from each other and adjacent segments can do the same. The movements in each case are quite small and rely on the membranes which connect the sclerites. These two combined actions cause an increase in size of the abdomen as a whole.

As the abdominal wall expands outwards, the air sacs inside are able to balloon out and the greater pressure outside the body pushes air into the sacs. Conversely, when the abdomen becomes smaller again, the air is pushed out of the air sacs. Muscles control the respiratory movements and these muscles are under the control of nerves from the ganglia. The build-up of carbon dioxide stimulates these nerves which then trigger the movements. So, respiration is driven by the build-up of carbon dioxide produced by the cells.

Resting or flying?

When a bee is resting or working quietly, most of the air flows in and out at the spiracles on T2, but when it is flying and needs a great deal more oxygen, the system changes: air is drawn in through the spiracles on T2 and the abdominal segments and pushed out mainly through the spiracles on A1 (the propodeum). The valves guarding the entrances to the spiracles have to coordinate during the process.

A beautiful system

The tracheal system is comparatively simple and adaptable to the widely differing life-styles of insects, but it would not cope with the energy demands of a bigger animal. Higher animals need a much more efficient transport system and, for this, the blood has been adapted as an oxygen- and carbon dioxide-carrying fluid. So, while you will be able to think of many similarities between your breathing system and that of your bees, the major difference is the use of your red blood to transport the gases between the tissues of your body and your lungs.

THE EXCRETORY SYSTEM

We saw, when looking at the circulatory system, that the haemolymph removes the waste produced by the cells as they work and also provides a reasonably constant environment around the cells. To do this, the substances in the plasma, and their concentrations, must be controlled. This is where the excretory system comes in. It is essentially a sophisticated filtration system which not only removes waste substances, which would slowly poison the cells, but also acts selectively, adjusting the amounts of particular substances in the haemolymph so that there is a balance between water and salts, and the osmotic pressure and acidity (pH) remain within narrow limits.

There are two types of waste produced by active cells:

- Carbon dioxide produced as a result of respiration and removed by the respiratory system.
- Nitrogenous waste resulting from the chemical reactions which go on in the cells involving proteins and other nitrogen-containing compounds. This waste is removed by the excretory system.

Essentials of the excretory process

There are four aspects to the excretory process:

1   Filtration of the haemolymph by a special organ.
2   Re-absorption from the excretory system of useful substances which would otherwise be lost.
3   Active secretion of substances into the system (grabbing them from the haemolymph and passing them into the system).
4   Complete removal of the end product to the outside of the animal's body.

The excretory structures

To enable all this to happen requires special structures with very thin walls which are in very close contact with the haemolymph. In the honey bee, and other insects, these are the *Malpighian tubules*. In the adult honey bee, there are 100 or more tubules, each long and thin, extending throughout the abdominal cavity where they are completely surrounded by the haemolymph and wave around like thin white cotton threads.

Each tube is built of a single layer of cells attached to a very thin basement membrane on the outside and, on the inside, extended into a 'fringe' of *microvilli*. (Microvilli are microscopic projections from a cell surface and, where they are closely packed together as they are in the Malpighian tubules, they are like the nap on velvet.) Around the outside of each tubule are widely separated muscle fibres and a good supply of tracheoles. The free ends of the tubules are closed and the other ends open into the region of the digestive system between the ventriculus and the small intestine. They develop as outgrowths from the proctodeum so they 'belong' to the hindgut.

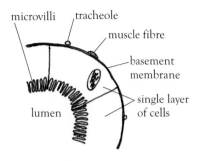

Section through part of a Malpighian tubule

How it works

Put simply, substances in the haemolymph are filtered through the wall of a Malpighian tubule at its upper (distal) end. (The muscle fibres cause the tubules to wave about and come into contact with the maximum amount of haemolymph.) First, the substances pass into the cells through the basement membrane and the cells pass them on to the open centre (lumen) of the tubule.

Filtration is a fairly passive, non-discriminatory process and a great deal of water will pass through. This is a problem because all animals living on dry land need to conserve water. So, as the materials travel along the tubule, some water is reabsorbed. Other substances, such as salts, may also need to be reabsorbed to keep the composition of the haemolymph constant. This is interesting because, at different times, the same substances may be waste or useful, so may be excreted or reabsorbed.

Finally, other substances are actively secreted by the cells. They pull passing molecules in and push them through into the lumen of the tubule. Reabsorption and secretion are active processes needing a lot of energy, and therefore oxygen, and this is why the Malpighian tubules need their supply of tracheoles. The lower (proximal) part of each Malpighian tubule is concerned with these processes of reabsorption and secretion. When the material in the lumen of the tubule reaches the intestinal connection, it passes

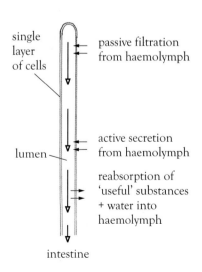

Malpighian tubule function

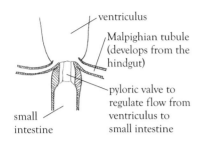

into the digestive system and, together with the waste from the digestive system, is passed to the outside of the body through the small intestine, the rectum and, finally, the anus. During its passage through the intestine and rectum, more water is absorbed from the gut contents.

The insertion of the Malpighian tubules

(redrawn from Dade, 1977)

Excreted substances

The simplest waste nitrogenous compound is ammonia but this is toxic and needs a large amount of water to remove it. Therefore, the normal form in which nitrogenous waste is excreted in most insects is uric acid. This is not so toxic and is not very soluble in water, enabling much of the water filtered from the haemolymph to be reabsorbed. In addition, there will be various salts, and any other substances which are harmful to the bee, in the final excretory product.

THE WORKER GLANDS

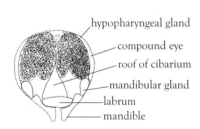

We cannot leave the internal anatomy of the honey bee without discussing some of the glands which are so important. There are two broad categories:

1   Endocrine glands which pour hormones into the haemolymph and are covered in Chapter 3.
2   Exocrine glands where the substances produced are passed to the outside. There are a number of these but we are only concerned here with five:

Front of a worker bee's head (cuticle removed) to show the main head glands

- hypopharyngeal glands ⎫
- mandibular glands   ⎬ found in the head
                                      ⎭
- wax glands
- Nasonov gland ⎫ these produce only pheromones
- sting gland   ⎬ and are discussed in Chapter 6
                         ⎭

The hypopharyngeal and mandibular glands

These are often called head glands or brood food glands and the diagrams show their position and appearance.

The role of the mandibular gland in the queen is discussed in Chapter 6 but, in the worker, these glands do different jobs at different stages of the insect's life:

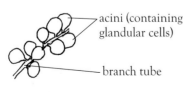

Small part of the hypopharyngeal gland

- in young bees they produce brood food and royal jelly.

- in later life the hypopharyngeal glands produce enzymes (invertase and glucose oxidase), used in converting nectar to honey, and the mandibular glands produce 2-heptanone which is a pheromone used in colony defence (see pages 108–9).

Production of all these substances is from glandular cells lining the walls of the mandibular glands and found within the acini of the hypopharyngeal glands.

The wax glands and wax production

When we start talking about wax, it is useful to realise that all insects produce it. The outer layer of the epicuticle is made of waxes which the insect uses in the same way that you use a waxed jacket – to keep out moisture. Some insects produce quite a lot of wax, scale insects are a good example and also those very irritating aphids which infest my cabbages every year. If you look at them closely, their little grey bodies are covered with white flakes of wax which offer some protection to these small, delicate insects. But honey bees are the champions of wax production. They make vast palaces from it, fashion it into beautiful, precisely measured cells, rear all their young in it and store all their food in it. In short, they use it to build their home. But where does it come from and how do they make it?

Glands and mirrors

The large amount of wax that the worker honey bee produces to make comb comes from four pairs of specialised wax glands. These are part of the body wall and are found within the four sterna of segments 4 to 7 inclusive in the abdomen. Each pair of glands is situated to the front of its sternum so that the sternum of the previous segment overlaps it.

    The gland itself is made of cells from the epidermis and these cells are columnar epithelial cells. 'Columnar' means they are shaped like columns. When the gland is functioning at its best (when the bee is 16–18 days old), the epithelial cells become much longer with spaces between them. So, put simply, each gland is a small thickened area of the epidermis. In the young bee and the older bee, the glands are thin. Below each wax gland is an area of the cuticle called a wax mirror (or plate). The base of each mirror is a transparent membrane and each is surrounded by a dark rim. The pair of wax mirrors on each segment looks like a pair of spectacles. The final part of the whole apparatus is a mass of fat cells and oenocytes which lie over each gland.

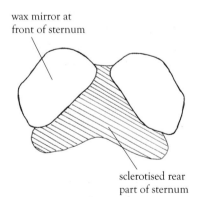

wax mirror at front of sternum

sclerotised rear part of sternum

The wax mirrors

These are hidden underneath the sclerotised part of the preceding sternum. They are found on A4, A5, A6 and A7

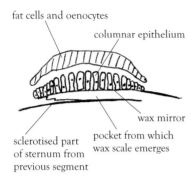

fat cells and oenocytes

columnar epithelium

wax mirror

sclerotised part
of sternum from
previous segment

pocket from which
wax scale emerges

**Section through a wax gland
from the side**

Production of wax

The ingredients for the wax are made in the oenocytes above the
glands. The components pass to the columnar cells of the wax
glands and a liquid pours into the spaces between those cells. This
then passes through the wax mirrors, which are perforated by an
enormous number of very fine canals (only apparent under an
electron microscope), and hardens to a small, transparent flake of
wax. This flake is extruded from the pocket made by the
overlapping sterna. At times, several flakes of wax may build up on
a single wax mirror. The bee removes the wax flakes with its hind
legs. It rubs the large basitarsus against the abdomen and the
scales stick to the brushes on the leg – usually. The bee can then
use its mandibles to mould and manipulate the little flake.

A chemical factory

To make the ingredients for wax, more than 300 of them, the bee
needs to consume a lot of nectar/honey. It also needs some
protein from pollen which it eats in the first few days of its life.
These materials are carried in the haemolymph, extracted by the
oenocytes and the raw materials for the wax are synthesised in the
oenocytes. The size of the oenocytes is directly related to the
thickness of the columnar epithelium. To allow wax production
to proceed, the bee needs an *incoming* supply of nectar and a high
temperature of about 35 °C. The fashioning of comb from the
thousands of flakes of wax is another story which you can find in
Chapter 7.

3 CONTROL SYSTEMS

All the bits and pieces that make up a bee (or any other animal) need to work together. The animal also has to be able to react to its surroundings so that it can interact with the world around it. As an example, consider what happens when you want to cross the road. First, you use your eyes and ears to assess whether it is clear or whether you are likely to be mown down by a bus. Then, if you think it is safe, the muscles which control your legs have to start working to enable you to walk across the road, step up onto the pavement and turn so that you do not flatten your nose on the wall at the other side, which your eyes have detected. You need to know where you are in space, which way up you are and, of course, all the time you have to breathe and your heart has to keep beating.

Similarly, our bees use their sense organs to let them know what is going on around them and their muscles to get them to their destination. This is all very complicated and in each case there is a nervous system co-ordinating everything, ensuring that stimuli are interpreted and acted upon correctly. In the case of breathing and many other essential functions, the control is automatic, but it is still there. There are also slow changes, involved with growth and development, and these, too, are co-ordinated, but this time by a chemical-based system called the endocrine (hormone) system. In the next few pages, we are going to look first of all at the bee's nervous system and its function and then at the endocrine system, which is often ignored but is vitally important.

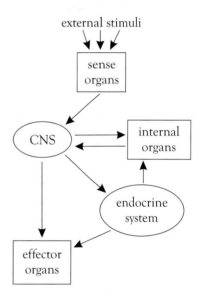

A simple diagram to show how control systems work

A BUNDLE OF NERVES!

Not a description of the average examination candidate, I hope, but an attempt to unravel some of the complexities of the nervous system. I like the definition of the nervous system given in my (fairly old) *Penguin Dictionary of Biology*: 'A mechanism which co-ordinates the various activities of an animal with each other and with events in the external world, by means of messages rapidly conducted from part to part'.

The nervous system is made up of three main components:

- nerves
- the central nervous system (CNS)
- sense organs.

To understand the nervous system, I think it is useful to look at its development. In the more primitive segmented worms, each segment is more or less autonomous and controlled by its own segmental *ganglion*, which is like a small, simple brain controlling its own segment, but, as animals evolved and conquered new environments, the front (anterior) end, which came into contact with changes in the environment first, became modified into a head. This part was the first to meet new stimuli, such as the early bird as the worm poked its head out of the ground, so it became equipped with specialised sense organs to receive the stimuli, and the ganglia in that region showed an increase in size and development in order to handle the mass of incoming messages from the sense organs. So the brain appeared. In the honey bee, the brain has reached an advanced stage of development, for an insect, and is capable of quite complicated processes including learning and remembering. However, many parts of the bee's body are still controlled from the modified segmental ganglia. Before we can understand the nervous system of the bee, it is essential to look at three aspects which are common to all nervous systems, including our own:

- the nerve cell
- initiation and transmission of impulses
- synapses.

The *nerve cell* or *neuron* (which can be spelt 'neurone' and comes directly from the Greek word meaning a nerve) is the unit from which the nervous system is built, so all parts of the nervous system are made up of nerve cells. Each cell consists of:

- a cell body, which looks much like any other 'normal' cell with a nucleus surrounded by cytoplasm.
- Processes drawn out from the cell body. There is usually a single long one called the *axon*. This carries the impulses to other cells and away from its own cell body. Other, shorter processes arise either from the axon or from the cell body itself and these are called *dendrites*. They carry the impulses

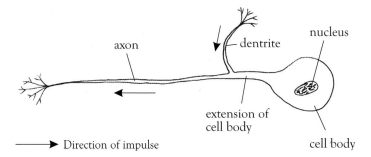

axon — dentrite — nucleus

extension of cell body

Direction of impulse

cell body

A basic nerve cell
(redrawn from Chapman, 1998)

to the cell body or to the axon. There may be one or many dendrites. At their ends, axons and dendrites branch to give many endings.

Neurons are called *afferent* if they carry impulses towards the central nervous system (CNS) from sense organs of various kinds, or *efferent* if they carry impulses away from the CNS to effector organs (organs which do things) such as muscles and glands, but there are, within the CNS, many nerve cells which pass impulses from afferent to efferent cells. These are the co-ordinating cells and are called *association neurons*. Cell bodies are found in the sense organs and near the surface of the insect, but they are concentrated in the various parts of the CNS.

Initiation and transmission of impulses

- A stimulus, which may be mechanical, chemical or visual, stimulates the ends of a dendrite (usually many dendrites from different neurons). Different dendrites respond to different stimuli so, for example, one activated by light will not be affected by a chemical.
- Changes occur in the membrane surrounding the dendrite and, providing they are strong enough, these pass along the dendrite and start an impulse in the axon. This impulse is always of the same strength and, once initiated, runs the full length of the axon. It can be likened to an electric current passing along the axon but moves more slowly and is produced by successive changes in the membrane along the length of the axon (or dendrite). This is a self-perpetuating mechanism which results in an impulse flowing very rapidly to the end of the axon.
- Once the impulse has passed a section of the axon, the changes in the membrane are reversed and the axon returns to its normal state so that it is able to conduct another impulse very soon afterwards.

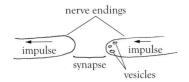

How a synapse works

Chemicals (neurotransmitters) are released from the vesicles when an impulse reaches them. The chemicals cross the gap and initiate an impulse in the next nerve ending

- Normally, a stimulus results in the production of many impulses in many dendrites of many cells and it is the number and frequency of impulses which determine the subsequent response, if any.

Synapses

What happens when an impulse reaches the end of an axon? Nerve cells do not join onto one another directly. There is always a microscopic gap which is called a *synapse*. When an impulse reaches the end of its axon it has to somehow 'jump' over the synaptic gap to the next dendrite. This is accomplished by chemical messengers which are stored in the end of the axon and are released when an impulse arrives. The chemical flows across the gap to initiate an impulse in the dendrite of the next nerve cell.

Building blocks

Now we understand the basic elements of a nervous system, we need to organise our neurons sufficiently to take the process further and see how they are built into the nervous system as a whole. The nerves connecting the major structures of the system are simply bundles of nerve fibres (axons and dendrites) from different nerve cells, so it should be clear that some of these fibres are very long, reaching from sense organs on the surface of the bee to the brain, for example. In fact, nerve cells, with their long extensions, are the longest known cells. The impulses whizz along the nerves and they serve as the roads in this information transport system.

THE CENTRAL NERVOUS SYSTEM

The second part of the system is the central nervous system (CNS) and we are going to look at this in detail. As the name suggests, this is the part of the system which is central to it (in the middle of the bee) and the part which co-ordinates all the activity of the whole system. There are three interconnected parts to the CNS:

- the brain and sub-oesophageal ganglion
- the segmental ganglia
- the ventral nerve cord.

The systems appear to be somewhat different in the larva and the adult but, in fact, they are not and the adult is simply a modification of the larval situation. As we have already seen, the arrangement in primitive segmented animals is to have a ganglion (or more accurately, a pair of ganglia) to control each segment and, in the honey bee larva, this is still the basic pattern although there has been some modification at the two ends of the animal. So, at the anterior end, the larva has a brain and a sub-oesophageal ganglion. Both of these structures are compound ones. Rather confusingly, the insect head was originally made up of six segments and each of these would have had its own ganglion. The brain is a structure derived from the ganglia of three primitive segments, which are no longer apparent, right at the anterior end. The sub-oesophageal ganglion is made up of the three ganglia from the segments giving rise to the mandibles, maxillae and labium. The brain is situated above the oesophagus and the sub-oesophageal ganglion is situated below it, the two joined by connecting nerve fibres thus effectively making one complex structure. At the posterior end of the larva, there is a ganglion in the eighth abdominal segment (A8) which is formed by fusion of those in A8, A9 and A10. The rest of the segments each have their own ganglia. The larva therefore has three thoracic and eight abdominal ganglia plus the complicated bit at the front end.

The only change in the adult is that some of the ganglia have fused so that only seven remain in total. This has come about by the fusion of ganglia in T2, T3, A1 and A2 (T = thoracic segment, A = abdominal segment) to make one very large ganglion which serves both pairs of wings and the middle and hind pairs of legs. There has been a further modification at the posterior end – the last ganglion is now found in A7.

In both larva and adult, all the ganglia and the brain are connected by the ventral nerve cord, which is a double cord containing nerve fibres.

It is of interest, but no direct significance to us, that in *Musca*, which is a large genus of flies containing the housefly, the ganglia are still further modified so that all the thoracic and abdominal ones have joined to form just one large ganglion.

Structure of a ganglion

This is basically very simple and consists of:

- an outer layer containing cell bodies
- an inner core (called the neuropile) containing nerve fibres, some of which form a network while others are collected into bundles.

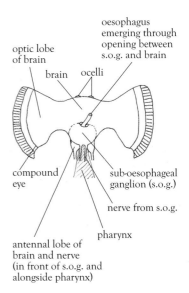

Brain and sub-oesophageal ganglion

(*posterior dissection*)

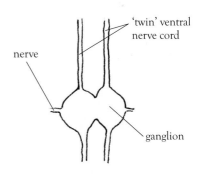

An abdominal ganglion

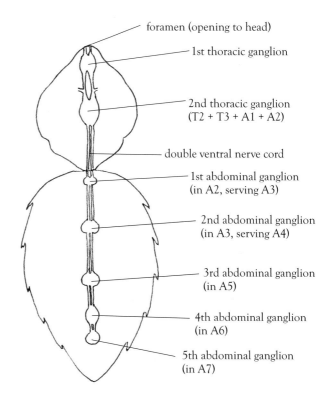

foramen (opening to head)

1st thoracic ganglion

2nd thoracic ganglion
(T2 + T3 + A1 + A2)

double ventral nerve cord

1st abdominal ganglion
(in A2, serving A3)

2nd abdominal ganglion
(in A3, serving A4)

3rd abdominal ganglion
(in A5)

4th abdominal ganglion
(in A6)

5th abdominal ganglion
(in A7)

The ventral nerve cord and ganglia of the worker honey bee

From the ganglia, nerve fibres extend to the sensory organs on the outer part of the body and other fibres go to effector organs, such as muscles and glands.

Structure of the brain

This can be divided into three parts (originally developed, as we have seen above, from three primitive segments):

- *Protocerebrum* which includes the optic lobes and the *corpora pedunculata* (mushroom bodies). These bodies are of particular interest in the honey bee where they are well-developed. They are the site of the more complex learning processes.
- *Deutocerebrum* which is mainly concerned with the antennae. Remember that the antennae are major sources of information about the outside world.
- *Tritocerebrum* which is a small part of the brain with connections to the sub-oesophageal ganglion and nerves serving the labrum and front part of the gut.

Division of labour between brain and ganglia

The CNS of the honey bee is a wonderful system, beautifully constructed to perform many complex tasks. In essence, it is similar to our own and at the pinnacle of development, as far as the insects are concerned. The brain is big, for an insect, and the 'higher' functions reside there, but, if a bee is decapitated, it is still capable of carrying out various activities which we would find impossible if someone chopped off our heads. For example, it can still move its legs and wings although the brain is needed for co-ordinated activity. This is because some activities are controlled by the ganglia, nerves from the large second thoracic ganglion passing out to the wings and the second and third pairs of legs. Nerves from the sub-oesophageal ganglion go to the mouthparts, but this structure is not solely concerned with control of feeding and nerves from the brain travel to the labrum and the cibarium. So, there are impulses whizzing about between the various parts of the CNS and along the ventral nerve cord.

It used to be accepted that the honey bee's behaviour was solely the result of inbuilt reactions and that there was a very simple relationship between stimulus and action involving no 'thought' on the part of the bee. More recent work is beginning to question this belief and appears to show that the honey bee is far more intelligent than we have given it credit for. It may think and make decisions about some aspects of its life in the same way as we do. Certainly, it is able to learn and remember. The mushroom bodies are the seat of these higher faculties. We are beginning to understand that the bee's brain shows a remarkable level of development and is a truly amazing structure, despite its small size.

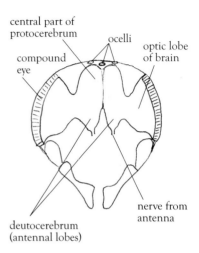

Brain (anterior view)

The hypopharyngeal glands have been removed to reveal the brain (see diagram on page 40)

MAKING SENSE OF IT

We will now consider the final large chunk of the nervous system, the sense organs.

All complex animals need structures, called sense organs, to enable them to know what is happening around them, find their food and mates, and detect enemies. We recognise the five senses of touch, taste, smell, hearing and sight. Animals also need to 'understand' their position in space and the movements that are going on in their muscles even though, most of the time, this information is not consciously appreciated. These internal sense organs are called *proprioceptors* and occur in the cuticle and in the muscles of the bee.

The brain is the centre of things

All that sense organs do is receive various stimuli, transform these into nervous impulses and send them on their way to the brain (or ganglia). So, we do not smell a rose with the sensory cells in our noses. Those cells merely send impulses to the appropriate part of the brain in response to the presence of particular chemicals which stimulate them. The brain then interprets these impulses as the smell of the rose. Similarly with sight – the light sensitive cells in the eye are activated by the light which falls on them, they initiate impulses which travel to the brain and are interpreted as a 'picture'. All very strange! The honey bee has a number of sense organs and we will look at each type in turn.

THE SENSILLA

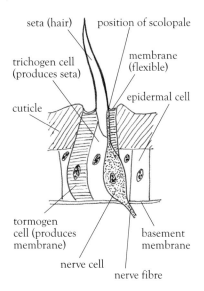

seta (hair)   position of scolopale

trichogen cell (produces seta)

membrane (flexible)

epidermal cell

cuticle

tormogen cell (produces membrane)

basement membrane

nerve cell

nerve fibre

A sensillum trichodeum

(redrawn from Dade 1977)

This is the collective name given to the individual sense organs in a bee (excluding the eyes). There are several different kinds of sensilla and thousands of each kind. Each sensillum reacts to only one, clearly defined, stimulus but the list of stimuli is long: touch, vibrations, relative humidity, carbon dioxide concentration, chemicals, stress in the cuticle and stretching in the muscles. This is not an exhaustive list and some categories can be subdivided. Problems arise when the student of bee anatomy tries to get to grips with the different types of sensilla because they are classified and named according to their structure and not their function. (This is mainly because their functions were unknown when they were named) To add to the confusion, they have largely unpronounceable, easily forgotten names which are impossible to spell. The names come directly from the Greek and therefore only mean something to a student of Greek! We will look at basic structure first and then go on to the detail.

Structure of a simple sensillum

As with everything biological, to understand how a structure works, you must first know how it is built. The diagram shows one type of sensillum. It is called a *sensillum trichodeum* because its principal structure is a hair (seta) and in the Greek language 'trichos' means 'hair'. This is the basic type. It reacts to the stimulus of touch but some of them probably react to other stimuli. The various structures are quite easy to understand:

- The *seta* (hair) is the part receiving the stimulus. When something touches it, it bends.

- The *membrane* is a thin flexible part of the cuticle which allows the seta to move.
- The *trichogen cell* produces the seta.
- The *tormogen cell* produces the thin membrane and fills the space beneath it.
- The *neuron* (nerve cell) is activated by the stimulus and sends an impulse along its axon to the central nervous system.
- The *scolopale* is a thin cap which contains the dendrites of the nerve cell.

Many thousands of sensilla are found on the antennae

How does it work?

When something touches the hair, it is bent over. This stimulates the dendrites in the scolopale and starts an impulse which travels along the dendrite and then along the axon to the central nervous system. Because there are many sensilla trichodea all over the bee, there will be many impulses generated and the brain, or ganglia, interpret these. Within the brain or ganglia, new impulses are then generated which go to muscles or other structures and, if the original stimulus is strong enough, action will be taken, eg, the bee will move away from something pushing it.

So far that is fairly simple, but we will now muddy the waters by looking at the way this simple structure is developed into more complex structures and investigating some of those long names. We will classify the sensilla according to the jobs that they do, but remember that they are named according to their structure.

Taste

The *sensilla basiconica* are sensitive to various chemicals. Each individual one may react to one chemical or to a group of chemicals. As well as being responsible for detecting taste they may also react to dangerous substances in the bee's environment. The common name for these structures is *peg organs*. The structure is very similar to the sensillum trichodeum but the hair is exchanged for a short, stiff, peg and there are three or four neurons at the base instead of one. Each neuron has a thin process (the dendrite) reaching into the peg. These peg organs are found on the antennae, particularly the last eight segments, on the mouthparts, in the mouth and on the legs. (It must be fun being able to taste things with your legs!)

Smell

The sense of smell is so fundamental to the life of the honey bee

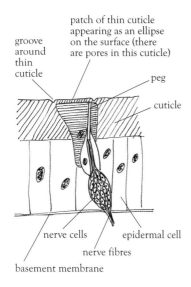

groove around thin cuticle

patch of thin cuticle appearing as an ellipse on the surface (there are pores in this cuticle)

peg

cuticle

nerve cells

epidermal cell

nerve fibres

basement membrane

Another type of sensillum – sensillum placodeum (plate organ)

There are probably 30,000 sensilla placodea on each drone antenna. Here they show as pale dots

that these sense organs occur in enormous numbers on the last eight segments of the antennae, particularly in the drone where there may be something like 30,000 per antenna. They are *sensilla placodea* or *plate organs* and their structure is quite simple to understand. Go back to the original diagram again, change the hair to a peg, as in the peg organ, then push this just below the surface of the cuticle. Cover the hole with a thin cuticle, marked by a line of unsclerotised cuticle into an ellipse. This thin cuticle is perforated by many minute pores which allow the passage of the molecules which are the stimulus. Now increase the number of neurons to about 20 and you have a plate organ.

Carbon dioxide levels, temperature discrimination, relative humidity (RH)

These are the responsibility of the *sensilla coeloconica*. These structures are similar to peg organs but with the peg sunk into the cuticle in a small cavity which is open at the top. They are therefore called *pit–peg organs*. There may be one or more neurons and it must be understood that each individual organ will react to only one stimulus. So a sensillum which reacts to carbon dioxide will not react to temperature or relative humidity, and vice versa. They are found on the antennae.

Cuticular stress

These receptors are called *sensilla campaniformia*. There is a small area of domed cuticle (like a shallow bell) with the nerve ending inserted into it (like the clapper in a bell) and there is one neuron. They are found, in small groups, on the mouth parts, antennal bases, bases of wings, the legs and the sting and they react to stresses in the cuticle.

Other stretch receptors

These react to various movements and muscle stretching and are the *sensilla scolopophora* (in some books these are called chordotonal organs). They differ from the other sense organs in that they are made up of groups of sense organs associated together. Typically, they are found at joints, for example, where the antennae join the head, the head joins the thorax, at the bases of the wings and in the legs. There are two large scolopophorous organs which have been given their own names:

- *subgenual organs* found in the tibia near to the joint with the femur. These are sensitive to vibrations from the surface upon which the bee is standing and also to loud airborne sounds.
- *Organ of Johnston* found at the distal end of the pedicel of the antenna (see diagram on page 11). Some of the dendrites are embedded in the wall of the pedicel and others are connected to the membrane between the pedicel and the first segment of the flagellum. It follows that a movement of the flagellum relative to the pedicel will result in the production of impulses. This organ is present in virtually all adult insects and its functions vary. In the honey bee, it appears to be a wind-speed indicator and to be used to assess a flying bee's speed of flight. It may also react to airborne vibrations which cause movement of the flagellum.

Touch and gravity

The *sensilla trichodea*, which we discussed at the beginning of this section, are found all over the bee's body and react to touch. Other S. trichodea are found concentrated between the head and thorax, thorax and abdomen and in the joints of the appendages. They enable the bee to 'know' its position relative to gravity.

Two more words for your mental dictionary:

- *chemoreceptor* is a general name for any sense organ which reacts to chemicals and includes those associated with smell and taste
- *proprioceptor* is any sense organ which detects changes within an animal's body so those that sense movement of muscles and stretching of the cuticle are included.

Well, I warned you about the long words but I do believe that life should always provide challenges!

EYES

Bees need good eyesight. Within the hive it is dark, but when they are outside in the big wide world, they have to see what is going on around them, avoid anything about to eat them, see where they are going and recognise the flowers that they depend on for food. They have two large compound eyes, situated on either side of the head, and three simple eyes found at the top of the head. We will look at the compound eyes first. Using these, the bee is able to

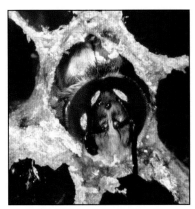

A hatching drone shows its huge compound eyes and three ocelli

primary pigment cells

corneal lens

crystalline cone made from 4 cone cells ⎱ light-collecting part

retinula cells

rhabdom (made of all the microvilli from the retinula cells) ⎱ sensory part

nerve endings

secondary pigment cells

The structure of a single ommatidium

(redrawn from Chapman, R. F. (1988). The Insects' Structure and Function. Taken from: Goldsmith, T. H. (1962) 'Fine structure of the retinulae in the compound eye of the honey-bee'. Journal of Cell Biology, 14, 489–94)

perceive movement, colour, patterns and polarised light, although it probably does not get as clear a picture of objects as we do.

Compound eyes are so-called because they are made up of many parts. Each part is called an *ommatidium* and functions as a complete unit, almost like a tiny complete eye. To give the bee a view of its surroundings, however, it needs all the ommatidia, giving it a mosaic-like picture. There are some 5000–6000 ommatidia in each eye of the worker honey bee (some books put it higher – either take your pick or get hold of a microscope and start counting!) but to understand how the eye works we only have to study one ommatidium.

We can split the component parts of any eye into two parts:

- A light gathering part, represented here by the lens and the crystalline cone.
- A sensory part which receives the light stimulus and changes it into electrical energy for onward transmission to the central nervous system. This part is composed of nerve cells and the nerve fibres which lead away from them.

So far it is quite simple, but the problem now becomes one of difficult words. Sorry, but I cannot do anything about that except try to explain them all. Look at the diagram of an ommatidium, then concentrate!

- The *corneal lens* is the part that is visible when you look at the surface of the eye. It is transparent to let the light in and takes on a hexagonal shape in surface view because there are so many packed together. The lens is quite thick and slightly convex each side.
- The *crystalline cone* lies immediately behind the lens and is a hard transparent cone tapering towards its inner end.
- There are two *primary pigment cells* (also called the *corneagen cells*) which are, as you might expect, pigmented. They lie along the outside of the crystalline cone preventing light from other ommatidia entering their cone so that each ommatidium is, in effect, an isolated unit. During the development of the eye, these cells make the corneal lens and then migrate to their final position.
- There are four *cone cells* (also called *semper cells*) which produce the crystalline cone during the development of the eye. The cytoplasm in the cells becomes transparent and hard, so forming the cone. In the mature ommatidium, the remnants of the nuclei of these cells remain.

So far we have dealt with the light-gathering parts of the

ommatidium and the cells which produce them. Now we have to look at the sensory part of the structure.

- The *retinula cells* are elongated nerve cells and there are eight full-length ones and one short one which extends only part way along at the inner end. The cells are twisted round one another along their length.
- The *rhabdom* is the 'core' which runs through the retinula cells. It is a space which is filled by the margins of the retinula cells which, at this point, are modified into many finger-like projections (*microvilli*), closely packed together and at right angles to the long axis of the cell. The part of the retinula cell modified in this way is called a *rhabdomere* and all the rhabdomeres together make up the rhabdom.

Think of a carrot! Imagine it to be the area of an ommatidium behind the crystalline cone. The outer orange part would represent the retinula cells (eight at the top and nine at the bottom) and the inner core would represent the rhabdom. Now imagine that the fibres in the core, instead of running vertically as they do in a carrot, are short projections sticking out of the orange part into this core area. Give the orange area a bit of a twist (many of the carrots I grow are like that anyway) and there you have a rough and ready idea of an ommatidium.

Now back to the bee's eye.

- *Secondary pigment cells* (doing a similar job to the primary pigment cells) surround the retinula cells, so isolating the ommatidium All the light entering it is 'kept within' that ommatidium and cannot 'leak' to its neighbours.
- *Nerve fibres* from the retinula cells conduct nerve impulses away from the cells after the light falling on them has stimulated the rhabdomeres.

If you think that was complicated, we will now try to sort out how it all works!

The single ommatidium

This is a complete unit. The corneal lens and the crystalline cone together concentrate the light striking the surface of the ommatidium into a single beam. This beam of light travels to the rhabdomeres and strikes the microvilli. Within the microvilli is a photopigment called *rhodopsin* (you have the same stuff in the light-sensitive cells at the back of your eye). When light falls on the microvilli, the energy contained in the light is used to change the molecular structure of the rhodopsin. (The changed rhodopsin is quickly converted back again into its original form using energy released by respiration.) Now a slight complication arises because there are differences in the wavelength of light to which the different retinula cells react. Sensitivity is as follows:

- two are sensitive to green light
- two are sensitive to blue light
- two are sensitive to ultraviolet light
- two are sensitive to either blue or green light
- one (the short one) is sensitive to ultraviolet polarised light.

In each case, there must be sufficient light energy to initiate the molecular changes, but this amount is very small.

The nervous connections

Each retinula cell has a nerve fibre leading from it. Nerve impulses are generated in each cell by the change in the rhodopsin. These impulses pass along these nerve fibres and eventually, by fairly complicated routes which need not concern us, reach the brain, where all the impulses together are interpreted and the bee 'sees'. (Some people find this difficult to grasp but if we take the human eye as an example, the eye may form a good image within itself, but if the optic nerve connecting it to the brain is cut, the individual will be blind in that eye. It is the brain which sees by interpreting the image formed in the eye.)

The eye as a whole

Each ommatidium acts as an insulated unit but the bee views its world through all of them together. Each one points in a very slightly different direction to its neighbours and so will receive its own individual quota of light. So, what does the bee see? Probably a mosaic made up of 'dots' from the thousands of ommatidia, so not the complete, clear picture which we see (or assume we see!). Patches of colour and shapes can be seen well and so can movements (try flapping your arms about in the vicinity of an active hive). Other adaptations help the bee in its unique world:

- The sensitivity to ultraviolet light is useful when dealing with many flower patterns
- The ability to use polarised light is important in navigation when the sun is obscured.

- The bee's eye is able to separate a moving picture into its component parts very rapidly. So a bee watching a film would see it as a series of individual frames separated by periods of darkness whereas we see it as a continuous picture because our eyes are not able to separate out the different images sufficiently rapidly. The bee is said, by technical types, to have a high flicker–fusion frequency of above 100 times per second (compared with our 20 times per second). This enables it to see rapidly moving objects better. These will include other flying insects and the ground rushing past when it is in flight.

Vision and the bee's life-style

The vision of the bee has developed to help the bee in its particular life situation. It is a flying insect which needs to navigate over large areas and react to dangerous situations, and which depends for its food upon flowers. Perhaps we should just mention that drones need particularly good vision to find queens when they are flying high above the ground. The drone's eyes occupy most of the surface of his head and are even bigger than those of workers and contain more ommatidia (probably 7000–8000). As a final point, it is nice to know that there are hairs around the surface edges of each ommatidium. These seem to be sensitive to wind speed, helping the bee to assess the flying distance to areas of forage.

The ocelli

Before we leave the sense of sight, we have to look at the ocelli which are often called the simple eyes.

There are three of these found on the top, towards the front, of the head in the worker and queen. In the drone, they are relocated on the front of the face because the compound eyes are so big that they meet in the middle of the top of the head. Each ocellus is made up of a lens produced by a thickening of the cuticle (as in the ommatidium). Beneath the lens are transparent cells and, below them, a number of retinula cells form rhabdomeres and a rhabdom, just as in the ommatidium. The retinula cells have their nerve fibres leaving the structure at the base.

It therefore has the structure of a simple eye, but the interesting thing is that the lens does not focus the light onto the retinula cells, so no image can be formed. The ocelli seem to be concerned with the perception of differences in light intensity.

Some simple experiments have shown that, if a honey bee's ocelli are covered, the bee starts foraging later in the day and stops earlier and that it responds more slowly to changes in light intensity.

Strangely, if the compound eyes are covered, the bee shows no reaction to light at all and behaves as though it was blind. So it may be that the ocelli have a stimulatory effect, increasing the response to light stimuli received by the compound eyes.

THE ENDOCRINE SYSTEM

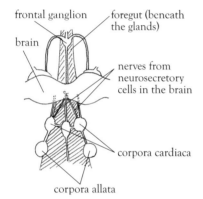

The general position of the main endocrine glands in an insect (dorsal view)

(redrawn from Snodgrass, 1956)

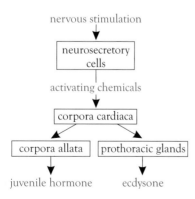

Interaction between the parts of the endocrine system

Which is the honey bee system that the average student never gets around to learning about? Which system is usually described at the back of the textbooks? Which system contains a few small and apparently insignificant glands which, in fact, control many of the major developmental and metabolic changes that go on in the honey bee? Answer: the endocrine system.

The endocrine system consists of a number of (ductless) glands, producing secretions called *hormones*, which are released directly into the haemolymph and have a profound effect upon growth, development, moulting, caste determination, age polyethism (performance of various tasks at different ages in the worker honey bee) including age at start of foraging, and glandular development. This is not a complete list of the effects of these important chemicals and there are certainly other functions of the system as yet undiscovered. Hardly an unimportant system! It works in combination with the nervous system, the latter controlling the rapid, minute-by-minute activities of the organism, while the hormones are more concerned with slower, long-term effects.

The glands of the endocrine system, although quite distinct, work together and sometimes hormones from different glands may produce contradictory effects.

The comments made so far apply as equally to the endocrine system of higher animals, such as us, as to honey bees except for some obvious differences – our babies do not shed their skins as they grow and we females do not develop into physiologically different castes depending on the food we are given as babies, for example! Because parts of the system only function in the larva, we will look at that first.

There are four major parts to the system:

- the neurosecretory cells
- the corpora cardiaca
- the prothoracic (thoracic) glands
- the corpora allata.

These are not isolated structures and there is much interaction between them.

Neurosecretory cells

These are found in groups in the brain and the ganglia. They are special nerve cells which are identical in structure to other nerve cells, have processes which conduct impulses but, as a result of stimulation, secrete chemicals which travel down the nerve fibres to various organs or to other endocrine glands.

The corpora cardiaca

These two glands are found behind the brain, one each side of the aorta, and are connected to the brain by the fibres of neurosecretory cells. The chemicals produced by these cells are stored in the corpora cardiaca and, when the conditions are right, they are released into the haemolymph, so we can think of the corpora cardiaca as a conduit for the chemicals produced in the brain. They also produce hormones of their own.

The prothoracic glands

These two glands are found between the pro- and mesothorax near the first spiracle and they produce and secrete *ecdysone* (moulting hormone). The production of ecdysone is essential for moulting but it is only released in response to another hormone, which is produced in neurosecretory cells in the brain, stored in the corpora cardiaca, and subsequently released by them into the haemolymph. This illustrates well the connection between the nervous and endocrine systems because this brain hormone seems to be released as a result of the reception of impulses in the brain, possibly related to size and stretching in parts of the cuticle.

The corpora allata

These are found on either side of the oesophagus. They are connected to the brain by the fibres of neurosecretory cells which have come via the corpora cardiaca and are also connected, by nerves, to the sub-oesophageal ganglion. They produce the vital hormone called *juvenile hormone* (often shortened to JH) and release it into the haemolymph. This used to be called neotenin and you may find this term in older books. High levels of JH in the larva maintain the larval characteristics and it is only when levels of JH fall and ecdysone is released that moulting occurs and growth and developmental changes are able to take place (see Chapter 4). So here is an example of the interaction of two quite separate hormones from different glands having an effect on one developmental process. JH also plays an essential part in the determination of the female castes but we will look at this in Chapter 5.

So far we have considered the endocrine system in the larva and it can be seen that it has a vital effect on development and metamorphosis, but what of the adult bee? All except the prothoracic glands, which degenerate at pupation, persist in the adult. Accounts of the functions of the system in the adult are sketchy and most work has been done on juvenile hormone which appears to influence a number of things:

- glandular development
- age polyethism
- foraging age
- defensive behaviour
- reproductive behaviour.

There may be other effects, as yet not researched.

How do they work?

Hormones circulate in the haemolymph and are broken down by enzymes. They are not stored in the glands where they are produced so there must be continuous production where a sustained effect is required. When a hormone reaches a target cell it causes biochemical changes, usually resulting in the production of enzymes which allow specific reactions to take place and/or enable production of particular proteins. The interesting thing is that one hormone may have different effects on different parts of the insect at different stages of its life, and so the target cells will also vary.

The endocrine glands must not be regarded in isolation but as a complementary control to the nervous system. The neurosecretory cells are part of the nervous system and long processes connect these groups of cells with the corpora cardiaca and the corpora allata. Nerves also connect the corpora cardiaca with the thoracic glands and with the corpora allata, so that there is an intimate connection between the two systems.

Finally, a thought to leave with you. Just be thankful that, although our hormones have many diverse effects on our lives including our growth and development, at least they don't cause our children to burst out of their skins at regular intervals.

4 BREEDING

In this chapter, first of all we are going to look at genetics and the peculiarities of the honey bee and, second, I will try to shed some light on the reproductive systems of queen and drone. Right at the beginning of Chapter 1 we defined a cell. In this chapter we will see that most cells fall into one large group making up most of the body of the honey bee (or any other animal). These are called *somatic cells* ('soma' means 'body'). However, there is one group of cells which is different – these are the reproductive cells, or gametes, normally called eggs or spermatozoa.

SIMPLE(?) MENDELIAN GENETICS

Well, as simple as I can make it! We start with a question: what is genetics? If I return to my trusty *Penguin Dictionary of Biology*, genetics is defined as the 'study of heredity and variation; of the resemblances and differences between organisms'. This is a good, concise definition and we should always keep it in mind as we grapple with the strange new words and ideas we shall meet.

Gregor Mendel was an Austrian monk who lived in the nineteenth century. He laid down the basic principles of modern genetics by carrying out many experiments with various plants, most famously peas, and observing and recording the way that defined characteristics such as colour and height were distributed in the population as a whole. Not much to do with beekeeping there you might say! But, from his observations, he formulated laws which explain the way in which characteristics are passed down from generation to generation in all plants and animals and these are as applicable to bees as to anything else. Mendel was also, incidentally, a beekeeper. I guess being a monk left plenty of time to pursue pet interests!

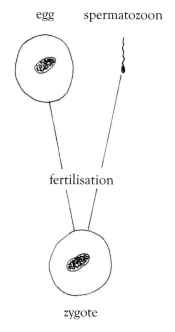

egg   spermatozoon

fertilisation

zygote

The essential elements of sexual reproduction

An egg is large and immobile (chromosomes = n)

A spermatozoon is small and active (chromosomes = n)

A zygote is a single cell produced by the fusion of an egg and a spermatozoon (chromosomes = 2n)

The real problem with genetics is the language. Suddenly you are confronted by a whole new set of words and, without understanding their meaning, all information might as well be in Chinese Mandarin (OK, so there's always one, but most of us do not read Chinese Mandarin!). So, we will start with some words and their meanings.

Chromosome

This is a structure usually shaped like a short thread, and found in the nucleus of every plant or animal cell. The number of chromosomes is constant in each somatic cell of every member of a particular species. In man, for example, it is 46. I have 46 chromosomes in the nucleus of every somatic cell of my body and so do you. In honey bees, the number is 32. Chromosomes occur in pairs, the two in each pair being identical in shape and size and often visibly different from all the other pairs. The chromosomes in such a pair are called *homologous chromosomes*. They are like identical twins. Often, for reasons which will become clear later, geneticists refer to the number of chromosomes in a particular species as a set number of pairs. All of the somatic cell nuclei of my body would be said to have 23 pairs of chromosomes. The honey bee would have 16 pairs.

Diploid

Diploid refers to a cell containing the full number of chromosomes. In a honey bee, a diploid cell would contain 32 chromosomes. The diploid number is denoted by the abbreviation '2n'. Although the term really applies to a cell, it is often used, loosely, to describe a whole organism. Using this idea, we can say that worker and queen honey bees are diploid.

Haploid

Haploid means that a cell contains half the diploid number of chromosomes. The gametes are haploid. In this case, there will be one chromosome from each homologous pair (16 in the honey bee) present in the cell and, again, the term may be used to describe a whole organism in which the cells contain this number, in this case the drone honey bee. The abbreviation 'n' is used to denote the haploid number. Many insects have haploid individuals or phases.

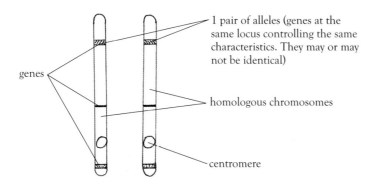

1 pair of alleles (genes at the same locus controlling the same characteristics. They may or may not be identical)

genes

homologous chromosomes

centromere

Diagrammatic representation of homologous chromosomes, genes and alleles

Only three gene positions are shown. Other genes will extend along the whole length of the chromosomes

Gene

The genes are the units of inheritance which are passed from one generation to another and each is part of a chromosome. Each chromosome carries many genes along its length and, in any complex organism such as a bee, there will be many thousands of genes in total. Each one is accurately duplicated whenever a cell divides and, although this process sometimes goes wrong (resulting in a mutation), genes are remarkably stable structures. Genes are made of deoxyribonucleic acid (DNA). An individual gene controls one characteristic, or process, in the organism and is always found in the same position on a particular chromosome. This position is called its *locus* (Latin for 'place'). The genes of a honey bee will determine everything about that insect – its development, its characteristic appearance and behaviour as a bee, its size, colour and everything else that you can think of. In many instances, several genes, acting together, will determine a particular characteristic. (The complete set of genes, the genome, of *Apis mellifera* was released on 7 January 2004.)

Allelomorphs (alleles)

Allelomorphs (usually shortened to 'alleles') are pairs of genes occurring at the same locus on homologous chromosomes. Going back a few paragraphs, we described homologous chromosomes as being like identical twins. Now, we all know that identical twins do have slight differences and so do homologous chromosomes because individual genes can occur in more than one form. There are often only two forms of a particular gene, when we can call them an *allelomorphic pair*, or there may be several forms. They are then called an *allelomorphic series*. The alleles control the same characteristic but have different effects on it. It is important to realise that, of the pair or series of alleles, only one representative can occur on any particular chromosome and the cells of any

1
Normal cell.
Chromosomes
not apparent

4
Chromosomes
arrange themselves
in the middle of
the cell

2
Chromosomes
become visible
in nucleus
(2n=2)

5
Chromosome
halves separate
and move
along spindle

Mitosis

Diagrams to show mitosis in a cell with one pair of homologous chromosomes

3
Chromosomes
replicate.
Spindle starts
to form

6
Nuclear membranes
reform. Cytoplasm
divides to give two
cells identical to
parent cell

individual can only have two, one on each of the pair of homologous chromosomes. The rest of the series will be distributed throughout the population.

Gametes

A gamete is a reproductive cell. A female gamete is an egg and a male gamete is a sperm. Each gamete is haploid (n), carrying one of each pair of homologous chromosomes and one allele from each pair or series. At *fertilisation*, the male and female gametes join together to produce a single cell containing the full number (2n) of chromosomes and two from each pair or series of alleles.

Mitosis

Mitosis is division of a cell nucleus. A multicellular organism such as the honey bee starts life as a single cell following fertilisation. That cell divides into two, those into four, and so on. Before each cell division, the chromosomes and all their genes are duplicated so that each new cell produced carries an identical set of chromosomes and genes to its parent cell. Each chromosome thickens to produce another one and then these separate into the

1
Chromosomes
become apparent
in normal cell
(2n=2)

4
The pairs separate
along the spindle.
Each chromosome
is still effectively two

2
Chromosomes
replicate so that each
one is effectively 2
chromosomes stuck
together. Membrane
round nucleus has
disappeared

5
Spindles form at
right angles to
original one. The
2 parts of each
chromosome
separate

3
The homologous
pair(s) of
chromosomes lie
together, connect in
1 or 2 places and
exchange material
(crossing over).
A spindle forms

6
The nuclear
membranes reform.
Each nucleus contains
1 chromosome from
each homologous pair.
The cytoplasm of the
cell also divides to
give 4 cells

Meiosis

*Diagrams showing meiosis in a cell
with one pair of homologous
chromosomes*

two new nuclei. Look at the diagram and it should become clear!
Something which sometimes causes confusion is the fact that
chromosomes only become visible as 'threads' during cell
division. The rest of the time, when the cell is not dividing, they
are dispersed throughout the nucleus of the cell.

Meiosis

Meiosis is a special kind of nuclear division which occurs only
once during the production of gametes and results in nuclei
containing half of the normal number of chromosomes and
genes. (Meiosis is often called a reduction division.) The result is a
haploid cell. The importance of this is that male and female
gametes carry one of each homologous pair of chromosomes and
when they join at fertilisation, the normal diploid number is
restored.

The number of chromosomes must always be kept constant
and, if the gametes contained the diploid number, the
chromosomes in the resultant cell would double. Because, during
meiosis, each pair of homologous chromosomes separates, so do
the allelomorphic pairs so that the gamete only carries one of each
pair of alleles which were carried by the parent. Also during
meiosis a strange phenomenon called 'crossing over' occurs. The

chromosomes within an homologous pair join together in one or two places and exchange some material. This leads to a recombination of genes in the chromosomes.

Meiosis actually starts off in exactly the same way as mitosis, with the chromosomes duplicating themselves. It is at this stage that some material is exchanged between them. They then separate, moving away from one another. Following this, the two halves of each chromosome separate and move away. The rest of the cellular material divides so that the final result is four cells, each with a nucleus containing the haploid number of chromosomes. Again, the diagram should help!

In practice, when eggs are produced, only one of the cells becomes a fully formed ovum with a large amount of cytoplasm, the others are very small in comparison, and degenerate.

This brings us back to Mendel and his laws of genetics.

The First Law or *Law of Segregation* states that allelomorphs segregate (ie, separate) when gametes are produced.

The Second Law or *Law of Independent Assortment* states that the distribution of the members of one pair of alleles between gametes has no influence on the distribution of members of other pairs, providing they are on different chromosomes. (Genes on the same chromosome may be linked together.) This law tells us that, if we imagine two pairs of alleles (A, a and B, b), gametes may contain AB, Ab, aB or ab and these combinations will be represented in equal proportions.

INHERITANCE IN THE HONEY BEE

The genes which a bee inherits from its parent(s) determine all its characteristics. Appearance is a fairly simple matter and the colour markings of an individual from a particular race of bee will be pre-determined by the genes which that individual carries. Behaviour is more complex and the genetic blueprint is modified by environmental factors both inside and outside the hive. As an example, the age at which worker honey bees perform certain tasks in the hive is basically controlled by their genes but weather, availability of food and the condition of the colony have effects which can override the message of the genes and may, for instance, send a worker out into the big wide world as a forager at a much younger age than that at which it was 'programmed' to go. It is recognised that defensive behaviour (temper to you and me!), disease resistance, hygienic behaviour and foraging behaviour are all controlled to some degree by genes.

Alleles often show a simple dominant/recessive relationship. A good example of this is the gene which produces the orange body colour which is referred to as 'cordovan'. In an individual worker or queen honey bee, there will be a pair of alleles controlling colour. If only one of these is the cordovan gene, the bee will have normal colouring for its race and will show no trace of orange coloration. The effects of the gene are hidden and it is said to be *recessive* to its companion which is, conversely, said to be *dominant*.

Remember that these two genes will appear at the same locus on homologous chromosomes so that, if they are present in a queen, each egg that she produces will contain only one of them. It is normal to represent genes by letters so that, in this instance, we can label the 'normal' dominant gene as 'C' and the recessive cordovan gene as 'c'. The genetic make-up of a queen carrying both genes would be 'Cc' and she would be said to be *heterozygous*

C = dominant gene for normal colour.   c= recessive gene for orange (cordovan) colour

100% of females will be heterozygous but will look normal
100% of drones will be hemizygous normal

An example of the results of a mating between a queen and drone involving dominant and recessive genes for colour

Queen's genes	Drone's genes	Offspring's genes = genotype		Offspring's colour = phenotype	
		Female	Male	Female	Male
CC	C	100% CC	100%C	100% normal	100% normal
Cc	C	50% CC 50% Cc	50% C 50% c	100% normal	50% normal 50% cordovan
cc	C	100% Cc	100% c	100% normal	100% cordovan
CC	c	100% Cc	100%C	100% normal	100% normal
Cc	c	50% Cc 50% cc	50% C 50% c	50% normal 50% cordovan	50% normal 50% cordovan
cc	c	100% cc	100% c	100% cordovan	100% cordovan

Summary of the outcome of the possible matings between bees with dominant (C) and recessive (c) genes for colour for this pair of genes. Her eggs would carry either 'C' or 'c'. A female honey bee would show the orange colouring only if she had two cordovan genes, ie, if her genetic composition was 'cc'. She would then be said to be *homozygous* for this gene. A normally coloured honey bee with the genes 'CC' would be homozygous for the dominant gene. Homozygous queens would be able to produce only one kind of gamete with respect to this pair of genes.

Here are two more words for your dictionary:

- *genotype* is the genetic make-up of an individual, ie, the genes it contains
- *phenotype* is the physical expression of the genotype.

So, using the same example, we would describe the genotype of a queen carrying the 'Cc' genes as heterozygous for the cordovan gene but we would describe her phenotype as normal coloration. A 'CC' queen would have a different genotype but her phenotype would be the same.

Not all alleles show this clear cut dominant/recessive relationship and there may be co-dominance or a series of alleles (although an individual will only ever have two from the series) which give a graded, rather than an on/off effect. To confuse the matter still further, many characteristics are controlled by more than one pair, or series, of genes.

Parthenogenesis and drones

A drone develops from an egg which has not been fertilised. This egg is haploid and has 16 chromosomes. It follows, then, that all the cells in a drone's body will be haploid. This has interesting consequences because it means that for every allelomorphic pair or series, a drone will carry only one gene instead of the two that his sisters will carry. He is described as *hemizygous*. If we go back to our example of cordovan coloration, a drone carries either C (normal) or c (cordovan). So he will show cordovan colouring if he inherits the single c gene from his mother, although she may appear completely normal.

It also follows that, when the drone's sperms develop, there will not be a meiotic division because there is already only a single set of chromosomes in each cell. In fact, meiosis begins with the duplication of the chromosomes but then the two halves of each chromosome will separate, giving two cells with the same (haploid) number of chromosomes in them. There will be no exchange of genetic material because there is only one of each pair of homologous chromosomes represented. Thus, as far as genes are concerned, all the gametes produced by a drone will be

The sex allele series can be represented as S_1–S_{12} all at the same locus on homologous chromosomes

If queen is S_1S_6 and drone is S_4:

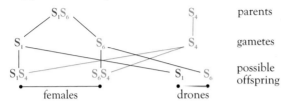

But if an S_1S_4 queen mates with an S_1 drone:

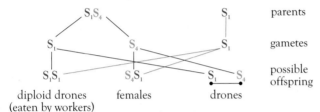

The remaining alleles will be distributed throughout the population and will function in exactly the same way

Diagrams illustrating sex determination and the production of diploid drones

identical and also identical to all the other cells making up the drone.

Sex determination and diploid drones

Now we have an added complication. Although we usually state that drones develop from unfertilised eggs and females (queens and workers) develop from fertilised eggs, it is not quite so simple.

Whether an individual honey bee becomes a male or female is determined by a series of sex alleles. The exact number is not known but it is between 6 and 18. All females are produced from a fertilised egg. This is diploid and therefore carries two genes from the series. Providing that the two genes are different (the individual is heterozygous), a female will develop. Drones are usually produced from unfertilised eggs which contain the haploid number of chromosomes (16) and so have only one gene from the series. However, if a fertilised egg contains two identical genes from the series of sex-determining alleles, the result will be a diploid drone.

This is most likely to happen when the egg and the sperm come from two closely-related individuals and are therefore likely to be carrying identical alleles. These eggs will be laid in worker cells (because they are fertilised eggs) and the resultant larvae will be eaten by the workers soon after hatching, leading to a poor brood pattern and a reduction in the number of workers raised (if raised artificially, the drones are infertile).

This problem tends not to arise under natural conditions because mating normally takes place between unrelated individuals well away from the nest and, because each queen mates with an average of 13 drones, the effects of a single, closely related mating are minimised. However, problems can arise where bees are inbred using instrumental insemination. In the most extreme case of brother/sister mating, 50% of diploid eggs may be homozygous for the sex genes, thus producing diploid drones and resulting in the loss of half of the queen's output. In the diagrams I have assumed 12 sex alleles and randomly selected three for the purpose of illustrating the point.

Now that we have looked at the way that characteristics are controlled by genes and how they behave (although we have only scratched the surface), we will look at the way those characteristics are handed on to the next generation in the reproductive process.

REPRODUCTION

Honey bees have two types of reproduction. One is colony reproduction, which we call swarming and will discuss in Chapter 7, and the other is the production of large numbers of new bees. Of course these two processes are closely related because, without a large population of bees, there can be no swarming. In this section we will look at this second type of reproduction with all its intricate and fascinating parts.

Female reproductive system

When we have a group of non-beekeeping people gathered round an observation hive, they always want to see the queen, and to marvel that all the other bees in the hive are her sons and daughters. Now, she may be called a queen and may be superior to the other bees in many ways; she may be a truly remarkable insect, but I think she has a pretty rotten life! Never allowed out of the hive except at the beginning of her life or with a swarm, her prime job in life is to lay eggs in vast numbers. And just think of being surrounded by all those children! She is, of course, very similar to all the worker bees in the hive, after all they all start life as a single fertilised egg, and it is only feeding which sets the queen apart. However, besides all the anatomical and behavioural differences between her and her daughters, the most important difference between them is the queen's fully-developed reproductive system and her ability to mate, enabling her to lay fertilised eggs which will develop into the workers needed to build up the colony.

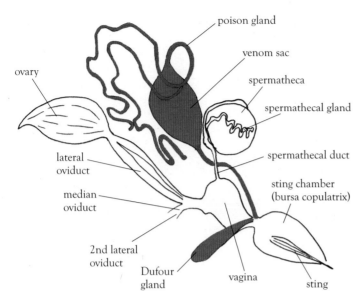

The main reproductive structures of a virgin queen from a lateral (side) dissection

(red-shaded parts are the venom system)

The parts of the system

The queen honey bee's reproductive system is much the same in general structure as that of any other species. Its function is to produce eggs, release them by a series of tubes to the outside and to receive the copulatory organ of the drone, and the sperm cells, during mating. There is a slight complication (isn't there always?) because the queen honey bee mates only at the beginning of her life. She has to store and preserve a vast number of sperm cells and have some kind of device for releasing them slowly over the whole length of her life, as needed. We will now look at the parts.

Ovaries

There are two ovaries, one on each side of the abdomen, occupying a huge amount of space. They are fixed by slender attachments to the ventral wall of the heart at their front end and are therefore situated above (dorsal to) the digestive system. The ovaries produce the eggs.

Oviducts

These are tubes, one leading from each ovary, down which the eggs pass after they leave the ovary. These *lateral* (side) *oviducts* join together to become the common, or *median oviduct* which is a very short tube leading to:

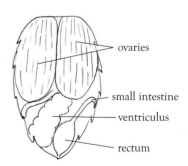

Dorsal dissection of a laying queen honey bee showing the position of the ovaries

The vagina

This is a wider tube, rather oval in shape, which ends in a narrow horizontal slit. As we shall see below, it has another duct opening into it on its dorsal side. Immediately below this second opening, on the floor of the vagina, is a fold of tissue called the *valvefold*.

The bursa copulatrix

'Bursa' originates from the Greek for a pouch or sac, so this is, literally, the mating pouch. This part may simply be called the bursa, or the sting chamber. It is a wide cavity opening to the outside of the body, with the sting loosely anchored to its top surface. On either side are two swellings called the lateral pouches.

The spermatheca

This is a round structure situated above (dorsal to) the vagina. There is a short *spermathecal duct* leading from it which opens into the dorsal wall of the vagina. On the outside surface of the spermatheca are a pair of *spermathecal glands*. These have ducts which have a single opening into the spermathecal duct just as it leaves the spermatheca.

Producing eggs

The ovaries are made up of between 150 and 180 egg tubes (*ovarioles*) and these can produce up to one million eggs during the lifetime of a queen. At the tip of each egg tube are cells called germinal cells which, by dividing, give rise to two types of cell:

- *oocytes* which will become eggs
- *trophocytes* (nurse cells) which accompany the oocyte and nourish it. There are 48 trophocytes with each oocyte.

Round each oocyte and its trophocytes there is a single layer of cells called *follicle cells*. These cells leave a small connection between the oocyte and its trophocytes.

As the oocyte passes down the egg tube it gets bigger, at the expense of the trophocytes which eventually collapse altogether. Yolk is added to the oocyte in the lower part of the egg tube. Yolk contains lipids, proteins and carbohydrates, some of which are made in the oocyte while others are made elsewhere in the body, particularly in the oenocytes of the fat body, and transported to the oocyte in the haemolymph. Finally, the follicle cells produce

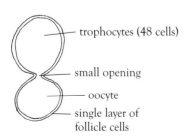

trophocytes (48 cells)

small opening

oocyte

single layer of follicle cells

An oocyte and its trophocytes

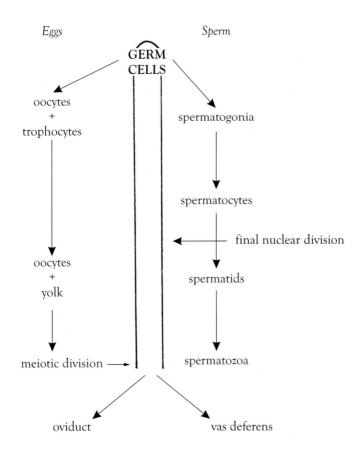

Eggs   *Sperm*

GERM
CELLS

oocytes
+
trophocytes

spermatogonia

spermatocytes

final nuclear division

oocytes
+
yolk

spermatids

meiotic division

spermatozoa

oviduct   vas deferens

**Very simple diagram to show
the development of eggs and
spermatozoa**

the outer covering (*chorion*) of the egg which undergoes its meiotic division as it leaves the egg tube and passes into the oviduct.

Laying an egg

Eggs are produced in the ovaries and pass into the lateral oviduct, then the median oviduct and the vagina. The walls of these tubes are muscular and the eggs are squeezed along. Finally, the egg passes into the bursa copulatrix and is deposited in a cell.

Boy or girl?

As we have seen, in honey bees, males (drones) are produced from unfertilised eggs and females (queens and workers) are produced from fertilised eggs. Because the queen mates only at the

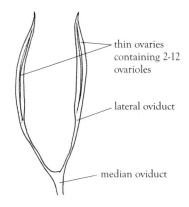

thin ovaries
containing 2-12
ovarioles

lateral oviduct

median oviduct

**The ovaries of a worker honey
bee from a ventral dissection**

beginning of her life, she stores all the sperm she will need in the spermatheca. To lay a fertilised egg, sperm must be released as the egg passes through the vagina. One of the sperm will then fuse with the egg. This appears to be controlled by the valvefold and a small, muscular pump in the spermathecal duct. This pump allows the release of a small quantity of sperm into the vagina and the valvefold, when raised, presses the egg against the opening to the spermathecal duct. If no sperm is released to fuse with the egg, an unfertilised egg is laid.

What about the workers?

Because workers are females too, they all have complete reproductive systems but in a very reduced form:

- their ovaries are small, containing between 2 and 12 egg tubes, and only able to produce a few eggs compared with the many thousands that the queen lays
- they are unable to mate
- their spermathecae are rudimentary
- if they do lay some eggs, these will all be unfertilised and will develop into drones.

In a normal colony with a laying queen, there will always be a few workers with partly developed ovaries containing a very few eggs. These workers will constitute between one and thirty per cent of the worker population, depending on which book you read. Such workers do not usually lay any eggs unless the queen disappears and all the brood has hatched. Under these circumstances, there is no queen mandibular pheromone and the pheromones normally associated with brood are also missing, so the controlling influences are no longer present and a few workers start to lay eggs. The mandibular glands of these laying workers also enlarge and they may become 'pseudo queens' eliciting much the same response from other workers as a true queen would.

In European strains of honey bee, laying workers usually appear 30 or more days after the queen disappears (sooner if there is no brood), while in African strains of bee they tend to start much more quickly – perhaps only five to ten days after the loss of the queen. Now I am going to contradict myself! I said above that workers can only produce drones, but the odd egg may develop into a female and this trait is very marked in the Cape bee, *Apis mellifera capensis*. In this strain, many workers, and even queens, can be produced by laying workers. It is thought that this is due to the production of a diploid egg by a recombination of the chromosomes after meiosis.

On the whole, being a female honey bee of either caste does not seem to be a bundle of laughs so next we will look at the structure of the drone and his seemingly carefree life.

Flying gametes

We have looked at the reproductive system of the queen honey bee and now we are going to get to grips with the corresponding system in the drone. The heading of this section is 'flying gametes' and this is really what a drone is. Because he is haploid, his cells are all derived from one gamete – the egg cell of his mother – and he is merely a machine for producing and delivering more gametes, ie, sperm cells, to a queen honey bee.

His whole structure is directed to this end. He is big with strong abdominal muscles which come into use when he mates, and big flight muscles to power his wings. He has larger antennae, carrying about ten times as many sense organs as a worker to allow him to detect queen pheromones more readily, and his eyes are huge, with far more ommatidia than the worker possesses. These are connected to larger optic lobes in the brain to interpret the messages coming from the eyes. These differences ensure that, having found a queen by scent, the drone can home in on her by sight.

Of course, many other structures are either missing or very small. He has no sting, no pollen-gathering apparatus, no Nasonov gland, wax glands or hypopharyngeal glands. His proboscis is short, his mandibles are puny and his mandibular and salivary (labial) glands are small. So, he has one function only – to mate with a queen – and most drones do not even fulfil this one.

The parts of the system

The drone's reproductive system is made up of a part to produce sperms and a series of tubes and structures to nourish them and transfer them into a queen honey bee. The major difference between the male and female systems is that, in the queen, egg production and laying is more or less continuous whereas in the drone the sperm are produced in large numbers, must be stored until needed, and are used all at once.

Testes

The two testes are the structures which produce the sperms and correspond to the ovaries of the female. If you dissect a drone

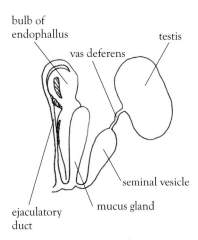

Dorsal dissection of a drone at emergence showing reproductive structures on one side only

(testis, seminal vesicle and mucus gland have been drawn aside)

pupa, the testes are big and, in fact, reach their peak size before the drone emerges from his cell. They then gradually shrink to become small triangular-shaped structures found towards the front (anterior) of the abdomen by the time the drone reaches full maturity at 12 days of age. Compare this with the ovaries of the queen which occupy most of her abdomen during the whole of her life.

Vasa deferentia (singular: vas deferens)

These are short curly tubes, with muscular walls, one leading from each testis to the next part of the system, the seminal vesicles.

Seminal vesicles

Seminal vesicles are really just continuations of the vasa deferentia but are much larger, rather like white sausages. They are sperm hotels where the sperms stay after travelling from the testes. They have muscular walls, lined internally by cells which produce a fluid to nourish the sperms during their stay.

So far, that is fairly simple. It is the rest of the system which makes life difficult!

Mucus glands

The most obvious structures when we look inside the abdomen of the drone are the two large, fat, mucus glands which form a U-shape and lie below the (smaller) seminal vesicles. They are not part of the main system of tubes and are not involved with sperm production or storage but are *accessory structures*. Again, they have muscular walls with a lining of cells which produce a liquid, but this liquid is different – it sets into a thick mass on contact with air. Two short tubes from the bases of the seminal vesicles open, one on each side, into the bases of the mucus glands.

Now we are back to our tubes forming the main part of the system.

Ejaculatory duct

This is a long tube which emerges from the inner side of the base of the 'U' formed by the mucus glands. The openings for this and the tubes from the seminal vesicles are very close together.

Still with us? Because the next bit is the cunning bit!

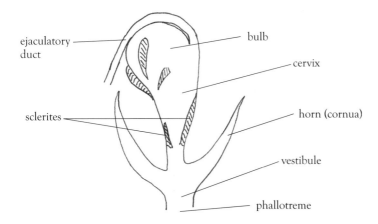

ejaculatory duct

bulb

cervix

sclerites

horn (cornua)

vestibule

phallotreme

The endophallus

The penis

The *penis* (also called the endophallus) is a complex and remarkable structure with several parts, situated inside the drone's abdomen. The ejaculatory duct opens into a very swollen structure called the *bulb*. This has various plates on its surface. Next comes a short narrow section of tube called the *cervix* and this opens into the final part called the *vestibule*. The vestibule has an opening to the outside, on A9, called the *phallotreme* and carries a pair of 'horns' (fancy name = cornua). The penis is situated inside the drone's abdomen with the ejaculatory duct opening into its anterior end.

Production of sperms

The production of sperms (or spermatozoa to give them their proper name) in the testes is very similar to production of eggs in the ovary (look back at the diagram in the female section on page 73). Each testis is made up of large numbers of fine tubes opening eventually into the vas deferens. At the top end of each tube is an area called the *germarium* where the original cells which give rise to the sperm are housed. They divide to produce cells called *spermatogonia*. As these move down the tube, they form groups enclosed in a membrane and are called *spermatocytes*. The spermatocytes grow in size and then divide (the incomplete meiotic division) to produce *spermatids*. Up to this point, the cells have a normal appearance but finally they change their shape, becoming long thin cells with a swollen 'head' end containing the nucleus. These are the fully formed *spermatozoa*.

Partially everted endophallus showing the vestibule and two horns

Mating

When the drone mates, the penis turns inside out. If, like me, you have trouble imagining this, get a rubber glove and pull one of the fingers inside it to represent the uneverted penis inside the drone. The opening represents the phallotreme. Imagine a tube (the ejaculatory duct) fixed to the end of the finger. Then blow air into the glove and squeeze it. The finger will shoot out. The tube would have been drawn through the finger and would now be inside it. The finger has been everted and is now outside the glove.

Back to the drone! The eversion of the penis is brought about by the squeezing action of the abdominal muscles. It is almost explosive and the structure is, at the same time, thrust into the queen's bursa copulatrix. The muscular linings of the seminal vesicles and mucus glands come into operation and expel first the sperms, followed by a mucus plug, and that is it. The endophallus breaks off and remains in the queen until removed, either by another drone or the workers, and the drone dies. The whole process is extremely rapid and the only part of the drone which survives is the mass of sperm which will now be stored by the queen.

Spare a thought!

So, when you next spear those drones on the end of your uncapping fork, stop to think what remarkably specialised creatures they are and do not dismiss them as simply a burden on the community. In the great order of things, as a means of carrying the characteristics of the colony on to the next generation, they are as important as the queen.

MATING BEHAVIOUR

So much for the anatomy and physiology of mating, but what about mating behaviour? There are a number of facts which form the basis of mating behaviour:

- mating takes place well away from the hive
- mating takes place normally between 10 and 40 metres from the ground
- drones from the colonies in an area fly to drone congregation areas during the middle part of warm summer days

- virgin queens fly to the drone congregation areas during warm summer days
- virgin queens mate with a number of drones (recent research suggests around 13 on average) over a period of a few days
- queens are able to mate only during the first four weeks of their lives.

Drone congregation areas are something of a mystery. They may contain thousands of drones from colonies all over the surrounding area and are found in the same places, year after year. How do the drones know where to go? After all, all the old drones die at the end of the summer so who shows the new boys the way? It is possible that the areas have particular characteristics which attract the drones such as:

- *Topographical features* which drones assess by sight and other senses. Congregation areas are usually over open ground and sheltered from the wind, but there are sites which are not.
- *Distance from apiaries*. The areas are usually at least 100 metres from an apiary.
- *Magnetic effects*. The Earth's magnetic field may be important. During the early part of their lives, drones develop large quantities of magnetite in their abdomens. This is a naturally magnetic iron oxide which can respond to magnetic fields. So maybe this is the answer.

A pursuit to the death!

When virgin queens enter a drone congregation area, they are chased by a group of drones. These are attracted by the queen's pheromones:

- *9-oxodec-2-enoic acid* (9-ODA) in the queen's mandibular pheromone attracts drones up to 50 metres downwind
- *tergite gland pheromone* attracts drones when they are within 30 cm.

As the drone approaches the queen from behind, his sense of sight becomes very important too. Having reached her, the drone moves above the queen, grabs her with all six legs and everts his endophallus (penis) into the open sting chamber. He then flips over backwards, the endophallus breaks off and he falls to the ground, dead or dying.

The sperms are still not at the end of their journey. Mating is such an explosive process that the sperms are propelled into the queen's oviducts where they are temporarily stored before being pushed up into the spermatheca. Here they are nourished and can survive for a long time. The movement from oviducts to spermatheca may take up to a day. The interesting thing is that most of the sperms are lost from the sting chamber and only a small proportion ever reach the spermatheca but, even so, every drone which mated with the queen will be represented.

Why is this system so complicated? It is fraught with dangers for the young queens which can so easily be lost on their mating flights, leaving a colony doomed to die out. The answers seem to lie in the need for the queen honey bee to mate with unrelated drones and to understand this we have to go back to diploid drones (see page 69). It is clearly essential that the queen does not mate with drones from her own nest and multiple mating with a number of drones and the storage of sperms from every drone minimise the problem. Additionally, there is some evidence to suggest that drones can recognise queens from their own nest and will prefer to mate with queens from other nests, but this has still to be proved.

5 GROWING UP

A honey bee begins life as an egg which turns into a tiny white larva. These two stages take place in open comb and we call them unsealed brood. When the larva is fully grown, the worker bees put a roof of wax over it and it undergoes a quiescent period when huge changes take place in its body. We call this sealed brood and at the end of this period a fully formed adult honey bee emerges from the cell. This is little short of miraculous and the change from the larval to the adult state is called *metamorphosis*. Because, in the honey bee and many other insects, the difference in structure and lifestyle between larva and adult is so extreme, we say that they go through *complete metamorphosis*. (Where the change is more gradual and the young resemble the adults in many, but not all, ways, for example in grasshoppers where the egg hatches into a baby grasshopper very similar to mum and dad, metamorphosis is said to be incomplete.) Complete metamorphosis seems strange until you realise that the larval and adult forms have completely different lifestyles. Put simply, the larva grows, the adult (properly called the *imago*) reproduces.

Of course, the honey bee is different and most of them do not reproduce as individuals, but you get the drift. This chapter will explain the development of the bee through the various stages of its life and look at the special problem of the development of the queen honey bee.

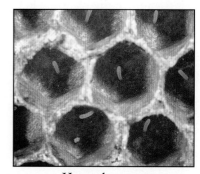

Honey bee eggs
They are about 1.6 mm long

THE EGG

Do you ever think of the amazing changes that take place between the laying of a honey bee egg and the appearance of a tiny larva? The rate and complexity of development is remarkable and, in looking at these early stages in the life of the bee, I am aware that I am only covering the basics because embryology (the study of the

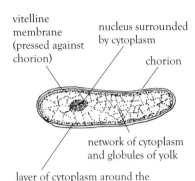

vitelline membrane (pressed against chorion)

nucleus surrounded by cytoplasm

chorion

network of cytoplasm and globules of yolk

layer of cytoplasm around the outside of the egg

Structure of the egg when it is laid

(redrawn from Snodgrass, 1956)

development of embryos) is a vast area of study on its own. First we must look at the structure of the egg when it is laid:

- *chorion* is the outer covering and the equivalent of a shell;
- *vitelline membrane* is the egg wall;
- *cytoplasm* forms a lining immediately inside the vitelline membrane. From this, strands spread throughout the middle part of the egg and these connect with a layer which surrounds the nucleus;
- *yolk* is found in the middle part of the egg, in large globules. It is enmeshed in the cytoplasmic strands;
- the *nucleus* is found near the slightly thicker end of the egg. Surrounded by cytoplasm, it contains all the genes which will control the development and characteristics of the bee.

Some basic facts

Before we start getting bogged down in detail, it is best to grasp one or two facts:

- think of the egg as a cylinder with closed, curved ends
- the ventral side is the convex side.

There are three main layers of cells (germ layers) found in an early embryo. These can be related to the structures which arise from them:

- *ectoderm* (outer layer) – cuticle and its appendages, tracheal system, foregut and hindgut, nervous system and sense organs, part of reproductive system, oenocytes
- *mesoderm* (middle layer) – muscles, circulatory system, part of the reproductive system
- *endoderm* (inner layer) – midgut.

Keeping those basic facts in mind, we can now go on to consider the development of the egg, which starts immediately it is laid. The changes can be listed in a, more or less, chronological order.

Stages in the development of the egg

1 *Cleavage.* The single nucleus divides forming many cells which are spread throughout the yolk.
2 *Blastoderm formation.* The cleavage cells move to form a layer immediately inside the vitelline membrane. This is called the blastoderm and everything else develops from it.

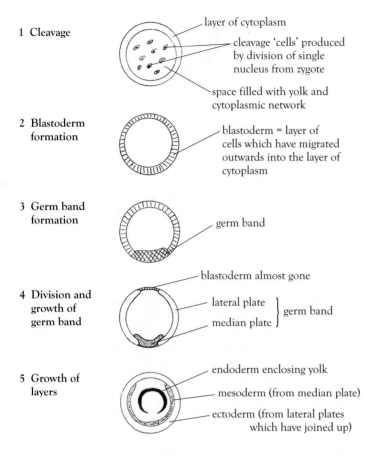

1 Cleavage
— layer of cytoplasm
— cleavage 'cells' produced
  by division of single
  nucleus from zygote
— space filled with yolk and
  cytoplasmic network

2 Blastoderm
  formation
— blastoderm = layer of
  cells which have migrated
  outwards into the layer of
  cytoplasm

3 Germ band
  formation
— germ band

4 Division and
  growth of
  germ band
— blastoderm almost gone
— lateral plate
— median plate ⎫ germ band

5 Growth of
  layers
— endoderm enclosing yolk
— mesoderm (from median plate)
— ectoderm (from lateral plates
  which have joined up)

Development of the egg
(All diagrams are cross-sections)
(redrawn from Snodgrass, 1956)

3 *Formation of the germ band.* A thickening of the blastoderm on the ventral side becomes the germ band. This gradually spreads all over the sides and ends of the egg.

4 *Division of the germ band.* Longitudinal fissures running the length of the egg divide the germ band into three areas; the two at the sides are called *lateral plates* and the one in the middle of the ventral side is called the *median plate*.

5 The median plate moves inwards towards the yolk and becomes the *mesoderm*. The lateral plates grow ventrally so that they join together and become the *ectoderm*, enclosing the mesoderm.

6 The *endoderm* forms as two ingrowths from the front and back of the blastoderm. These become separate structures, moving inwards, as two cup-shaped parts and then joining to enclose the yolk. This structure will become the ventriculus (midgut).

7 At the same time, ingrowths from the ectoderm appear. These will become the foregut and hindgut but, although they will be connected to the midgut, they will not join to it completely

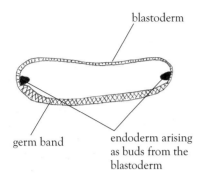

blastoderm

germ band   endoderm arising
                   as buds from the
                   blastoderm

**Longitudinal section through
the egg to show endoderm
formation**

(based on Snodgrass, 1956)

until after the larva 'hatches'. (In fact the midgut and hindgut connection will not be established until the larva pupates.)

Other changes are also taking place

- Two ventral thickenings of the ectoderm, running the length of the embryo in the ventral region, will develop into the nerve cord and the ganglia. The beginnings of the brain appear in a similar way.
- The tracheal system arises from pits in the ectoderm which grow inwards and eventually develop into the tracheal tubes and air sacs. The endocrine glands also originate from the ectoderm.
- The mesoderm develops into the linings of the body cavity, the muscles and the circulatory system. A small strip of mesodermal tissue at the dorsal side of the embryo forms a tube which becomes the heart and aorta, other mesodermal cells giving rise to the two diaphragms. The mesoderm is also the starting point for parts of the reproductive systems, although the outer parts, in male and female, come from the ectoderm, and the cells which eventually give rise to the sperm and ova are derived directly from the cleavage cells. That is important because it means that these vital cells undergo few cell divisions and cell division always has the potential to go wrong.
- The future legs, wings, mouthparts and sting of the adult insect are laid down as buds which grow outwards from the ectoderm (these will not develop fully until the pupal stage) and transverse constrictions along the length of the embryo mark the division of the body into segments.

After three days (approximately), the embryo has developed into a tiny larva which is now enclosed in a thin membrane called the *amnion*. The movement of the larva bursts the amnion and it then materialises as the chorion disappears. It may be that the chorion is digested by enzymes released by the larva but, whatever happens, the appearance of the tiny larva at the bottom of the cell marks the end of a truly marvellous period in the life of the bee.

THE LARVA

If we look first at the external structure of a larva, we see that it is an inactive, white creature. It is white because its cuticle is colourless and the white fat body shows through it.

Segmentation

The body is divided into a head and 13 segments. Of these 13 segments, the first three are thoracic (T1, T2 and T3) and the remaining 10 are abdominal (A1–A10). There are no constrictions between head and thorax, and between thorax and abdomen.

Appendages

Because a honey bee larva does not move, does not have to search for its own food and is protected from potential enemies, it does not need wings and legs, or sense organs to give it detailed information about its environment, so its structure is simple. It has no legs, no wings, no eyes, no antennae, no sting and very basic mouthparts. The legs, wings and antennae are present as buds beneath the cuticle, the very beginnings of the eyes are there but not visible and the rudiments of the sting and ocelli do not appear until the pupal stage. The beginnings of the mouth parts, the labrum above, mandibles and maxillae at the sides and labium below, surround the opening to the digestive system.

There is one extra structure, the opening from the silk glands. This is called the *spinneret* and appears to be in the labium. In fact, it is situated between the labium and the hypopharynx. The larva needs it to make its cocoon before pupation.

Internal structure

We can look briefly at the various internal structures and systems in the larva.

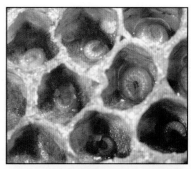
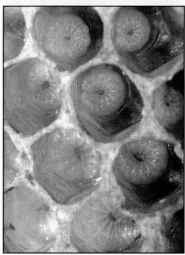

Worker larvae at various stages

(the ones in the lower photograph are older)

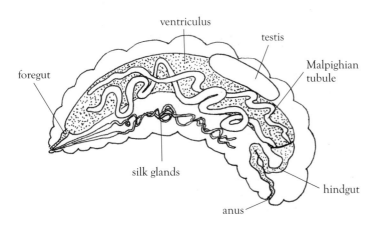

The internal organs of the drone larva

(side view)
(redrawn from Dade, 1977)

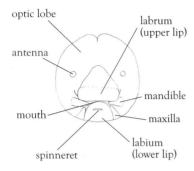

optic lobe

antenna

mouth

spinneret

labrum
(upper lip)

mandible

maxilla

labium
(lower lip)

The various 'adult' mouthparts, although visible in the larva, are not functional

- *Digestive system.* This is the most obvious system for the very good reason that the main aim of a larva is to eat and grow. The major structure is the true stomach or ventriculus (midgut). It occupies a large part of the larval body. The main point to remember is that the midgut and the hindgut (the last part of the digestive system) are not connected during the larval period, so no waste can pass out of the body. The rudimentary mouthparts of the larva have no function and it is only able to ingest semi-liquid food which it can suck in.

- *Excretory system.* There are only four Malpighian tubules in the larva. These grow thicker in the older larva as they fill with waste.

- *Respiratory system* (see page 35). This is clearly segmental without the adaptations we see in the adult. There are 10 pairs of spiracles from T2 to A8. Each spiracle is permanently open and leads into a short tracheal tube which connects with one of the two lateral tubes running the length of the body. These are connected at either end and by cross-tubes. There are no air sacs.

- *Nervous system.* This, too, shows the same segmental structure. The brain and sub-oesophageal ganglion are already formed from the ganglia of the segments making up the head, and the ganglia from A8, A9 and A10 are fused, but otherwise each segment has its own ganglion and nerve supply, enabling it to function pretty well independently.

- *Circulatory system.* The heart ends in A9 and extends forwards to the second thoracic segment. It has 11 chambers (one for each segment) and 10 pairs of openings (ostia). It continues forwards as a short aorta which is an inverted U-shape, open at the bottom. The dorsal and ventral diaphragms are present but the latter appears to break down in the older larva.

- *Fat body.* This fills most of the space in the larva and gives it its creamy white colour. It contains, in addition to the oenocytes and fat cells found in adults, *urate cells* which store waste.

- The *silk glands.* These are long, coiled structures lying near the ventral surface of the larva and opening to the outside via the spinneret.

- In queen and worker larvae, the ovaries begin to develop in the larva. In the case of worker larvae, they are very small but in mature queen larvae they are more than 2 mm long. The drone larvae have testes which are twice as big as this. Both the testes and ovaries lie near the back of the larva between A4 and A6.

The honey bee larva may look a simple creature, and in many ways it is, but, as with the adult bee, it is beautifully adapted to the life it leads which appears to be one of idle luxury and unutterable boredom!

THE PREPUPA AND PUPA

We have seen how the early stages of the honey bee develop from the egg and through the larval stage and now we come to the last piece of the jigsaw puzzle. In the remarkable life of the bee there is probably no period more miraculous than the pupal stage. Now I know you might groan and wonder what I am on about – how can this inactive colourless creature hidden away inside a sealed cell be so wonderful? But just think about what happens to it – a white grub with no legs or wings and a mouth which can only suck and lap fluids is transformed into a colourful creature with six complicated legs, wings which will carry it miles during its short life and mouthparts which will enable it to reach inside flowers and chew pollen and wax. There is also the acquisition of that pointy bit at the end which will enable it to become a killer. Quite a transformation. This dramatic change from larva to adult is called *metamorphosis*. So how does it happen?

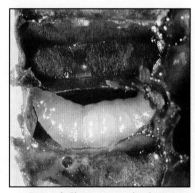

Once fully grown, the larva stretches out in its cell and the worker bees seal it over with a cap of wax

Sealing and spinning

We will look at the timings in the worker bee. After about six days, during which it is fed by nurse bees, grows rapidly and sheds its skin four times, the larva is fully grown, feeding stops and the worker bees cap over its cell so that it is no longer visible. Inside the cell the larva then stretches out straight with its head at the capping end and soon starts to spin a cocoon. This uses silk which comes from the silk glands. During this time, the join between midgut and hindgut opens and the Malpighian tubules empty their waste into the gut. All the waste is then passed out into the cell and much of it is mixed up with the silk making the cocoon – not very nice!

A partial moult

About two days after cell-capping, the larva undergoes its fifth moult, but this is not completed. The larval skin remains, surrounding the insect inside, which is now called a *prepupa* (or propupa). While the new cuticle, protected by the old larval skin,

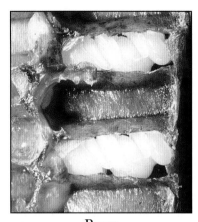

Pupae

They show the adult external structures except for the wings which are still small pads

remains soft and pliable, the external structures of the adult bee develop:

- the mouthparts elongate gradually
- the antennae appear
- the compound eyes, which have been faint structures in the larva, become more pronounced
- the sting begins to develop
- small legs appear, with their joints in place, and start to grow
- the wings appear as small pads on the side of the thorax
- segments A8, A9 and A10 are telescoped into A7.

It is important to realise that the structures such as legs, antennae and wings have begun their development during the later stages of larval life, but they are tiny and are formed inside the cuticle in little pits. During the prepupal period, they grow and then 'pop out' so that they are on the outside of the insect when, after about two days in the prepupal stage, the larval skin is finally shed, completing the fifth moult, and the *pupa* emerges.

An adult in-waiting

The pupa which emerges from the old larval skin resembles an adult bee in many ways, but is still white and is not hairy. Its wings are small, but its shape and all other structures are adult in form. But that is only the outside! The old internal larval structures are, for the most part, being broken down and the new adult ones are being built in their place.

The raw materials needed for this remodelling come from the larval breakdown and from the fat body, those reserves of protein, carbohydrates and fats which are accumulated in the body of the larva and then utilised during the prepupal and pupal stages of the bee's life. The adult systems are formed and the muscles are built. This is the reason for the earlier change in the exterior of the prepupa. The new muscles must have their exoskeleton framework in place before they can be built. Of particular importance are the huge flight muscles which were completely non-existent in the immobile larva.

We will look briefly at what happens to the various systems:

- *Digestive system.* This is almost completely broken down and rebuilt in the adult form.
- *Excretory system.* The four Malpighian tubules of the larva are destroyed and about 100 new ones are built.
- *Tracheal system.* This is largely unaltered except for an

increase in the numbers of small tracheae and tracheoles and the expansion of some of the large tracheal branches into air sacs.

- *Circulatory system*. There is little change.
- *Nervous system*. The brain enlarges, mainly due to the growth of the parts associated with the eyes and the antennae. The eyes are formed and the sensilla develop. There is fusion of some segmental ganglia so that the adult has only seven compared with the 11 possessed by the larva. Some nerves which serve muscles die because their muscles are destroyed; other nerves adapt to serve other muscles which are formed in the same location as old ones. New nerves grow and some original ones become longer.
- *Reproductive system*. The male and female reproductive systems begin their development in the larva and continue it in the pupa. They are not remodelled although they grow and changes take place, particularly in the drone, where the testes reach their full development during pupal life and then gradually shrink in size.

A drone pupa

The eyes of the pupa change colour gradually during development. The body colour darkens as emergence approaches

(This pupa is host to two varroa mites)

As the pupa develops, its colour changes. This is because the adult cuticle forms and gradually darkens inside the pupal cuticle which eventually loosens before being cast off completely in the final moult. The dark, hairy bee which emerges remains in its cell for a day or so, allowing its cuticle to harden and its wings and hairs to dry, before it chews its way out. The diagram should help with the timings of the various stages.

Still magic

Earlier, I described the pupa as a miraculous creature and I think that, even when we understand a little of the mechanism of metamorphosis, there is still an element of magic about it. The change from larva to adult, spread over a mere ten days from cell sealing to final moult, is immense and it is extraordinary that, in

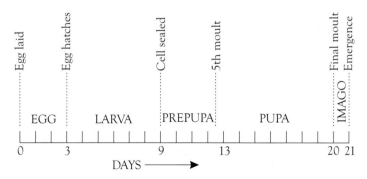

Egg laid — Egg hatches — Cell sealed — 5th moult — IMAGO — Final moult — Emergence

EGG   LARVA   PREPUPA   PUPA

0   3   9   13   20 21

DAYS ⟶

Development and metamorphosis of the worker

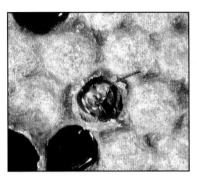

A worker bee emerges from
her cell after approximately
21 days of development

the vast majority of cases, it seems to happen without any major hitch so that we regard as commonplace the sight of a small furry head chewing its way out of its cell to begin a new life as an adult bee.

All the details I have given here apply to the worker bee and the timings are different in the drone and queen, but by mastering those for the worker initially, there is less risk of getting confused – at least that is the theory!

QUEEN OR WORKER?

When a sperm is released from the spermatheca of a queen it carries with it 16 chromosomes. As it fuses with an egg passing along the vagina, these chromosomes are added to the 16 which the egg is carrying giving a total of 32 and determining that the bee developing from this fertilised egg will be a female. The type of female into which it will develop has yet to be decided. Will it become a worker, destined to live a short expendable life of hard work, unable to mate and with undeveloped ovaries? Or will it become a queen, a larger individual who may live for years, is of vital importance to the colony, but whose prime function is as an egg-laying machine?

Type of cell

A female egg may be placed in a worker cell or a queen cell. A queen cell is bigger than a worker cell but that is only the beginning of the process. We know that an egg laid in a worker cell can become a queen if the cell is drawn out into an emergency queen cell or if the resulting larva concerned is moved into a queen cell. The cell itself is not the reason why one develops differently from the other although it may be the initial stimulus for the chain reaction which follows.

Development and
metamorphosis of the queen
and drone honey bee

Queen   Drone

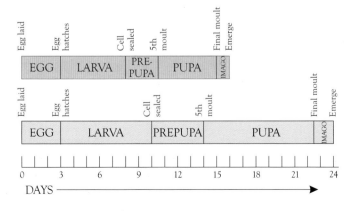

Larval food

There are three different components of the food which nurse bees feed to larvae:

- white, produced by the mandibular glands
- clear, produced by the hypopharyngeal glands
- yellow, derived from pollen.

The proportions in which these are fed varies depending on larval age and intended caste:

- first three days for a queen larva – mostly white food
- last two days for a queen larva – ratio of white to clear is 1:1
- average composition of worker larval food is white:clear:yellow in the ratio 2:9:3.

The white mandibular gland secretion has been shown to contain large amounts of pantothenic acid and biopterin and queen larvae not only receive a greater proportion of mandibular gland secretion but receive food about ten times as often as do worker larvae. So, brood food and royal jelly have different compositions at all stages of larval life. These facts would seem to be the key to the problem but, in fact, are not.

Importance of sugar

The amounts of sugar in royal jelly and brood food differ considerably. During the first three days of development, royal jelly contains 34% sugar, whereas brood food contains only 12% sugar. After three days, the sugar in brood food rises to 47% but this is probably due to the inclusion of honey in the food. Research has demonstrated that the sense organs on the mouthparts of larvae are sensitive to the sugar content of the diet and sugar probably stimulates an increase in food intake. It therefore appears that up to the age of three days, a queen larva consumes a greater quantity of food brought about by a higher sugar content. Furthermore, this food is of a different composition. But still we do not have the complete story.

The endocrine system

The glands of the endocrine system produce hormones which are secreted into the body. The paired corpora allata, situated on either side of the oesophagus, are part of this system and produce juvenile hormone (JH). The corpora allata of worker larvae which are grafted into queen cells at two days old increase in size dramatically and the level of JH in the haemolymph also increases. The high level of JH on the third day of queen larval development (ten times that in worker larvae) appears to be the trigger that leads to queen development.

Conclusion

High levels of juvenile hormone are the prime cause of the differentiation of female larvae into queens rather than workers, but the quantity and quality of royal jelly is also important. The sugar content of the food during the first three days of larval life is of importance in increasing the food intake and, somehow, there is a link between the type and, probably more importantly, the quantity of food and the enlargement of the corpora allata, with the consequent increase in juvenile hormone production. The type of cell may act as an initial stimulus for the nurse bees. This is summarised in the diagram.

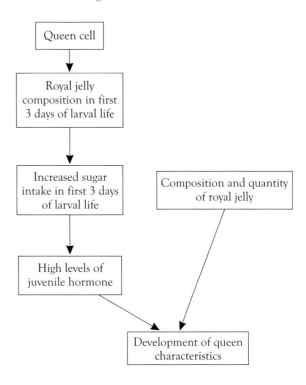

Factors involved in the development of queen characteristics in female larvae

6 KEEPING IT ALL TOGETHER

In this chapter we are going to look at organisation in the honey bee colony. We can think of a colony of honey bees as a 'super-organism' because it represents a further layer of development above that of the organism. Within an individual organism there is close contact between individual cells; those cells are modified to do particular jobs and the various parts are controlled by the nervous system (and endocrine system). However, in the super-organism there is no direct contact between the individual units (the bees), which all remain as discrete individuals, so control has to be maintained in different ways enabling the colony of bees to behave as a unit and ensuring that each individual bee is not 'doing its own thing' in isolation.

The colony is also a large family with one mother, the queen, her sons, the drones, and her daughters, the workers. All the drones are full brothers and are related to all the workers, but the workers are divided into groups of half-sisters because the queen mated with a number of drones. The biological aim of the super-organism is to grow, prosper and reproduce and each bee must behave in a co-operative way with its nest-mates to achieve these ends. In the first section we will look at division of labour among the major group of individuals making up the honey bee colony, the worker bees, and then we will go on to consider the various methods of control and communication that are used between individuals both inside, and sometimes outside, the nest.

The thousands of individual bees in a colony need to work together if the colony is to achieve its full potential

A MATTER OF AGE

Adult worker bees work at a large number of different tasks within the bee colony. It has long exercised the minds of researchers when and why particular tasks are carried out by an individual bee and this is the problem I hope to unravel in this section. I say

93

'hope' with some reason because this is a most confusing subject. Since my aim in this book is to simplify matters as far as possible, it makes life difficult!

First we will get rid of the long words: *age polyethism* is the technical term to describe the change in activities of the worker bee related to its age and *ontogeny* is the history of the individual development of (in this case) a worker honey bee. I will not mention them again!

When discussing the ages at which worker bees perform particular tasks, there are a number of vital facts to keep in your mind:

- the only constant is variability!
- the tasks performed depend on the conditions inside, and outside, the colony
- there is variation between individual bees
- the performance of many tasks is related to the development of the bees' glands
- all worker bees spend a large amount of time either resting or patrolling (walking round the nest).

In an ideal bee colony there is, however, a sequence of jobs which we can set out in a roughly chronological order:

1   cleaning cells
2a   brood rearing
2b   queen tending
3a   receiving and packing nectar/pollen
3b   comb-building
4   ventilation
5   guarding
6   foraging.

The most definitive statement that can be made is that 'summer' worker bees live for a maximum of 40 days and will spend roughly the first half of their lives inside the nest performing tasks 1 to 3. During this period they are called *house bees*. The remainder of their lives will be spent on tasks 4 to 6.

Relationship between tasks and gland development

House bees

Within this group, the very youngest bees (1–3 days) will be cleaning cells and eating large quantities of pollen. This intake of pollen results in the development of the *hypopharyngeal* and *mandibular* glands which produce brood food and royal jelly, so the next activity (3–15 days) is tending and feeding the brood and the queen. The age at which the two glands reach maximum output depends on the book you read! This group of bees are found near the centre of the broodnest because that is where their work is.

The large consumption of pollen is also essential for the development of the *wax glands*. Their development overlaps with that of the two brood food glands and bees will cap cells from an early age. The peak of wax production and, therefore, of comb-building will be a little later (10–18 days).

As the hypopharyngeal glands decrease in size, they switch from production of brood food to production of two *enzymes*, invertase and glucose oxidase. These two enzymes break down sugars in nectar and help convert nectar into honey. So, at this stage, the bee will be concerned with processing and storing honey (and pollen). Our worker is now probably 16 to 20 days old. Notice that all in this slightly older group of workers will be found towards the outside of the nest, building new comb and handling the colony's food.

Outside bees

From about 20 days onwards, the house bees move outside the nest. Some will work as the air-conditioning plant of the colony, maintaining an even temperature within and creating air currents to remove surplus moisture. Some of them can be seen fanning at the entrance. Others will act as guards at the entrance. Both of these jobs tend to be done by bees in the transitional phase between inside work and foraging but some bees may alternate foraging trips with spells as guards. To work effectively as guards, the bees need to produce the *alarm pheromone*, 2-heptanone, which comes from the *mandibular glands* after they have stopped producing brood food. This pheromone is used principally to repel invaders, particularly robbing bees. The *sting pheromones* and *venom* production also peak at around this time.

The final phase of a bee's life, approximately days 20–40, is as a forager and the *Nasonov* gland reaches maximum production at this time.

Resting and patrolling

Although the popular picture of a honey bee colony is one of constant, productive activity, worker bees in the nest spend a great deal of time apparently doing nothing. Some of them appear to wander aimlessly about; others actually rest, either in cells or on the surface of the comb. The aimless wanderers we call patrolling bees and their function seems to be to pick up clues about the condition and needs of the colony. They react to a huge number of stimuli but little is known about the way they work. Resting may also serve many functions. Certainly, bees producing beeswax and brood food may need to rest while more of the commodity is being formed in their bodies. It may also be that resting bees form a pool of workers which is available when there is a sudden surge in work, for example when a honey flow starts. (Remember that next time you are berated for nodding off!)

A flexible system

It is difficult to be precise about the activities of the worker bee. She can perform tasks as they are needed by the colony and is certainly not rigidly restricted to one particular job at a set age. It is certain that the development of the various glands is not governed solely by an inbuilt time-clock which switches them on and off at a particular age, but is influenced by colony conditions. One factor which has a major effect is the availability of pollen. Any one bee may perform many tasks over a very short period and some bees may not be involved in a particular job at all at any time during their lives. Some of the work that has been done on this topic is fascinating. Lindauer (and some of his hapless students) spent 176 hours watching one bee and recording every task that she performed. That is more than a week!

Undoubtedly there is still much to be learned by those who can stay awake and concentrate long enough to watch what goes on inside a hive and faithfully record it.

COMMUNICATION

We now come to consider the methods of communication between individual bees. Of course, if the bees could talk it would apparently make life simpler for them and us. Imagine being able to listen in to discussions about food shortages and intentions to swarm. Think how much easier life would become if you did not have to work out what your bees were going to do, and how it would take the wind out of the sails of those tiresome individuals who go on endlessly about being able to 'read' a colony! But bees cannot talk and, in the absence of speech, they have to use other methods of communication which we can only wonder at. It is important to remember that a bee's brain, although well-developed for an insect, is a very simple structure when compared with those of higher animals and much of what appears to be interaction between bees is a passive receiving of a small piece of information which results in a specific response in the recipient individual. The sum of all the individual pieces put together results in the apparently smooth running of the colony but we should not assume that all control is automatic, for it may be that bees are more intelligent than we give them credit for and that they are indeed able to make simple, informed, decisions.

Trophallaxis

The main methods of imparting information from one bee to another are:

- food sharing
- pheromones
- dancing
- vibrations.

Although I have listed these as separate processes, they all work together and it is often impossible to separate them. So pheromonal and food-sharing information may be transmitted at the same time, as may dancing and food sharing, and so on. A particular response may be made as a result of various different stimuli which may come from a combination of the methods above. Nothing about bees is simple!

An equal share for all

Larvae, queens and drones are all fed by worker bees but here we are discussing the sharing of crop contents between worker bees. Food sharing, or *trophallaxis* to give it its proper name, is a rapid means of spreading information throughout the colony. Several different research workers used radioactive or coloured nectar to show that nectar fed to a few worker bees was present in more than half the members of the colony within 24 hours.

The mechanism of food exchange is easily seen in the hive by any beekeeper. It starts with one worker begging for food or another offering it. A begging bee pushes its tongue towards the mouth of another bee. The other bee then opens its mandibles, pushes its tongue forward and regurgitates a drop of nectar from its crop, which the begging bee takes. An offering bee will regurgitate a drop of nectar and offer it to another bee. The result of this is that the crops of adult workers throughout the colony will contain the same mix of nectar and other substances at the same concentrations. While the bees make contact, their antennae also touch. So, as well as receiving or giving nectar, scent messages are exchanged.

Pathways of sharing

There is a tendency for food to pass from older, foraging bees to younger ones in the broodnest, and from those with full crops to those with emptier ones, but even bees with the same amount of nectar in their crops may share some. The process ensures that all the bees in the colony have a continuing appreciation of the quality of incoming nectar and pollen sources and their abundance within the colony. This will help to govern their behaviour in relation to brood rearing and to influence foraging behaviour. It will have a direct effect upon the egg-laying rate of the queen and on the ability of the nurse bees to feed larvae and it will also help to determine the division of labour between bees into house bees and foragers. An example may help. It has been suggested that when there is a large amount of pollen in the hive, the young bees will be well fed and their guts will have a high content of protein from the breakdown of the pollen. When foragers receive this high protein food during food sharing, it will inhibit further pollen gathering. The 'common colony stomach' also contributes to the unique colony odour which allows bees from a colony to recognise each other.

Bees which have been feeding and tending the queen tend to become more active food sharers for a time afterwards. This may be a means of spreading queen pheromones either in the food or by antennal contact.

Food sharing and dances

Another aspect of food sharing occurs in the round and waggle dances which worker bees perform to indicate the whereabouts of a source of nectar. The dancing bee gives the following bees 'samples' of the nectar which she has collected, usually in response to begging. This may help the recruited foragers to recognise the forage odour and certainly communicates information about the quality of potential foraging areas. More about that later.

PHEROMONES

Insects live in a world of aromas which we, with our poorly developed sense of smell, cannot even begin to imagine. Probably the most important scents are the pheromones. They are made in glands called *exocrine glands* (this means glands that secrete their substances to the outside of the body).

It is surprising to discover that our knowledge of pheromones is comparatively recent and the first one, in the silkworm *Bombyx mori*, was not identified chemically until the late 1950s. A definition was coined at that time and this still holds true today:

> *Pheromones are substances which are secreted to the outside by an individual and received by a second individual of the same species in which they release a specific reaction which may be behavioural, developmental or physiological.*

We will refer back to this definition later when we look at particular pheromones of the honey bee. In insects in general, pheromones have a great variety of functions such as selection of food plants, location of prey, transformation of solitary to gregarious phases, defence, courtship and mating behaviour, trail marking and social organisation. They may, artificially, be divided into two types:

- those triggering long-term, irreversible, physiological change
- those giving an immediate and short-lived response.

A great deal of work has been done with the Lepidoptera (butterflies and moths) and particularly with the pheromones which female moths release to attract males. There are practical spin-offs from this work in, for example, the development of pheromone traps for codling moth in orchards, so reducing insecticide use. Incidentally, in the lesser wax moth (*Achroia grisella*), unusually, the males produce a pheromone which attracts the females – but I digress!

A number of interesting facts emerge about pheromones in general:

- they are *produced* continuously by the gland concerned
- they are usually *released* under specific conditions but some may be continuously released
- they are usually mixtures of substances
- one pheromone may communicate a wide variety of information depending upon environmental factors and the condition of the recipient
- alarm pheromones usually contain substances which have low molecular weights and are very volatile so that their effect is short-lived.

The honey bee and its pheromones

We are particularly interested in the pheromones which help to co-ordinate the activities of the honey bee. Queens, workers,

A worker exposes its Nasonov gland while it fans its wings to disperse the scent

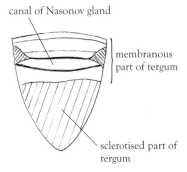

canal of Nasonov gland

membranous part of tergum

sclerotised part of tergum

Tergum of A7 of the worker honey bee to show the canal of the Nasonov gland

drones and brood all produce pheromones and comb probably also releases chemicals which act as pheromones, but our knowledge here is still incomplete. We will look at four pheromones in detail:

- *Nasonov pheromone* produced in the Nasonov gland of the worker and containing seven different substances.
- *Queen mandibular pheromone* (often called queen substance) from the queen's mandibular glands, with two principal components.
- *Alarm pheromone (1)* produced in the worker mandibular glands and containing one active substance.
- *Alarm pheromone (2)* from the worker sting, with eight constituents.

In each case, the chemicals are produced by glandular cells (this simply means cells which produce chemicals!) in the gland.

Nasonov pheromone

The Nasonov gland is found beneath the tergum of A7. It is normally hidden, but when the worker bee stretches its abdomen a pale thin strip can be seen between the terga of A6 and A7. This has a canal through which the pheromone percolates through tiny pores. The glandular cells are beneath this canal.

Mandibular pheromone

The mandibular glands are found above the mandibles and the glandular cells line their walls. The pheromone drains down onto the base of the mandible through a duct and it then travels along a groove to the functional end. The basic structure is the same in worker and queen although the pheromones are different.

Alarm pheromone

The alarm pheromones produced in the sting apparatus probably come from clusters of cells near the bases of the lancets, but no one seems too sure about them! The pheromone is released when the sting is extended, even though it may not be employed to sting anything.

What do they do?

Comparing the four pheromones described above with the list of properties given earlier, some interesting facts emerge. The multiplicity of function of a pheromone is demonstrated very clearly by queen mandibular pheromone which has an enormous range of activity and crops up in all sorts of different situations: it inhibits queen-rearing, worker ovary development and worker egg-laying; stimulates foraging behaviour and the release of Nasonov pheromone; enables workers to recognise the queen; attracts drones on mating flights and workers to a swarm cluster. Notice that it functions in different ways in different situations and has long-term physiological effects as well as immediate behavioural effects. In some circumstances, it also works in conjunction with other pheromones produced by the queen from different glands and in conjunction with pheromones produced by workers. Another interesting thing about this pheromone is that, although it is made up of quite a number of different chemicals, only two appear to have any real function. These are:

- *9-oxodec-2-enoic acid* (usually abbreviated to 9-ODA)
- *9-hydroxydec-2-enoic acid* (9-HDA).

Sorry about the names!

On the other hand, Nasonov pheromone has only one well-defined function in marking/orientation, although this operates in many different circumstances. So, workers use it to mark a potential new home, to attract flying bees to a swarm, to attract the queen back to her hive after mating, to mark unscented food sources, to 'call-in' stragglers after disruptive hive manipulations and in other situations where an attractant is needed. The chemical occurring in the greatest quantity is geraniol, but this is not the most active ingredient. The other six chemicals in the mixture are all related to geraniol and some are produced by its breakdown. It may be that in different situations different combinations of chemicals are used or the importance of individual chemicals within the mixture varies. There are also other pheromones involved in marking/orientation, particularly the footprint pheromone produced in the worker's tarsus which she spreads wherever she walks, and these may work on their own or with Nasonov pheromone, enhancing its effect.

Honey bees also produce alarm pheromones. The weakest is 2-heptanone, produced in the worker mandibular glands and its primary function is to repel robbing bees at the hive entrance – a kind of bee equivalent of pouring barrels of hot oil from the battlements! The other chemicals, causing aggressive or defensive behaviour, are all produced from within the sting and are much stronger. The first to be identified was isoamyl acetate and, as most of us are painfully aware, this stimulates stinging behaviour in other bees. It is probable that the full combination of the

Guard bees at the entrance to a hive soon release alarm pheromones when they are alerted to danger

chemicals in sting pheromone is necessary for the complete effect and/or that different chemicals elicit slightly different responses.

An incomplete picture

Remember that there are many more pheromones produced by honey bees. Some we know about, such as the footprint pheromone produced by queens and workers, but others are only assumed because of the action they cause. No doubt further information will be discovered in time and we will have a more complete picture of the complicated chemical world of the honey bee.

A slightly different aspect

The definition of a pheromone that I gave at the beginning of this section specified that the effect of a pheromone was felt by an animal of the same species, but there are situations where other species can also detect the pheromones produced by an individual and react to them. Where the resultant effect is to the benefit of the other species, the chemical is called a *kairomone* and where it is to the benefit of the insect emitting the pheromone, it is called an *allomone*.

So, a chemical given off by drone brood can attract varroa mites, to their benefit, and then is called a kairomone. To take this one step further, think of the effect of opening a defensive hive. What are the alarm chemicals doing? As soon as the bees open their sting chambers you will detect the smell and close the hive rapidly. In this instance, the chemicals will be functioning as a pheromone, inducing other inhabitants of the hive to defend their home, as an allomone because it is sending away a potential predator – you – and as a kairomone because, as a result of receiving it, you will leave the hive alone, so avoiding an attack by the bees. So everybody wins thanks to one mixture of pheromones!

DANCES AND VIBRATIONS

In this final section on methods of communication, we are looking at vibrations and that most extraordinary phenomenon – bee dances. Worker bees perform a number of different dances, both inside and outside the hive. Their use when locating food sources is particularly important because it allows the colony to make the most efficient use of its surroundings. Imagine being a worker honey bee coming out to look for food. You can travel up to five kilometres or so from your hive (although you will be much more productive if you work close to the hive), so you have a total area of about 1900 hectares – just think about it! Unless you are 'told' which patch of flowers to head for you will waste most of your time looking about – and you only have about 20 days to live! Therefore there are several dances associated with foraging. The other colony activity where dances and vibrations are particularly important is swarming.

The round dance

This dance is used when there is a source of food near to the hive and its message is 'go out and hunt around the immediate neighbourhood'. This is the dance which is used when we carelessly leave honey exposed in the apiary in July, or leave the dirty extractor uncovered near to the hives. It can lead to an outbreak of robbing because bees given this message will look at all potential sources and may try to get into other hives nearby. Equally, it is used when the hives are very close to a forage source such as a field of oilseed rape.

Waggly tails and a transition

As the forage source gets further away, the round dance changes to the wagtail dance, but not abruptly. In between is the intermediate sickle dance. The forage distance at which these dances are used varies from one race of bee to another, but the wagtail dance is always used where the forage is greater than 100 metres from the hive. This dance gives information about the distance, direction and quality of the forage. It is simply a figure of eight with a straight run between the top and bottom of the '8'. During this straight run, the dancing bee buzzes her wings and rapidly shakes her abdomen from side to side (hence the name of the dance).

Because the dance is performed on the vertical face of a comb, but transmits information which is horizontal, the vertical always represents the direction of the sun (wherever it is) and the angle that the straight run makes with the vertical represents the angle of the forage to the sun. (Some, more primitive, species of the genus *Apis* build a special horizontal comb where they dance because, presumably, they have not developed the ability to translate vertical dancing to horizontal food finding.) The distance of the forage source is communicated by the length of the straight run and the number of circuits completed per unit time.

The round dance
Message: food is nearby

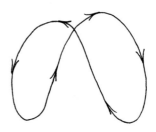

The sickle dance
There is a gradual transition from round to wagtail dance as forage distance increases

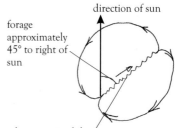

direction of sun

forage approximately 45° to right of sun

bee wags its abdomen as it moves along the line; length of line is equivalent to the distance

The wagtail dance
This communicates distance, direction and quality of a forage source

Bees gather round a forager
performing the wagtail dance

The watching bees also learn something about the quality of the source, in terms of sugar content, by the enthusiasm of the dancer, how long she dances and how vigorously she wags her abdomen. The samples which the dancing bee provides for the watchers also give information about quality and help the foraging bee to find the flowers involved. The vibrations are particularly important and have apparently evolved in bees which nest in dark cavities where they cannot see what is going on. By observing the wagtail dance performed by scout bees and other foragers, our tyro will be able to simply fly away, using the information on distance and direction to find a good source of food.

A feature which I find delightful is that these dances are performed on a particular area of comb, just inside the hive, which is called the 'dance floor'. Here the dancers perform and recruits go to watch them. This conjures up for me a picture of twirling ball gowns, music and excitement – but then my imagination occasionally runs away with me!

Dancing to a different tune

There are a number of other dances now recognised and probably the best known is the *dorsoventral abdominal vibrating dance* (DVAV dance). This is used when more foragers need to be recruited during a nectar flow and is particularly obvious in the early morning. The dancing bee rushes up to another bee and either pushes its head against her and grabs her with its feet, or mounts her. The dancing bee then vibrates its abdomen up and down (as opposed to side to side in the wagtail dance). Bees so treated move down to the dance floor and observe the wagtail dances and are recruited to foraging duties. Many of these bees may be those which are resting or patrolling.

This DVAV dance is also performed on mature queen cells, helping to keep the queens inside, and on queens during queen-cell construction, and it probably has a role in timing swarming and mating flights and, particularly, in the emission of afterswarms (casts). It appears to have several diverse uses but it is possible, as more work is done, that subtle differences may appear in the dance under different conditions.

Swarming and dancing

As well as the DVAV dance which helps to determine the timing of swarming, and the wagtail dance which is used to indicate the location of possible new homes, other dances are associated with swarming.

These include the *buzzing run* (Lindauer called this the Schwirrlauf, which I think is much more fun), where a bee runs in a straight line across the comb, buzzing due to rapid vibrations of its wings, until it collides with another bee. The two make contact with their antennae, the frequency of the buzz increases and when they end their contact, they both run off in different directions to repeat the process. This, not unreasonably, results in increased activity in the colony, followed by the emergence of the swarm. (Imagine similar behaviour in a closely packed crowd of people.) Buzzing runs again take place before the swarm takes off to move to its new home and the dance may then be referred to as the break dance (a bee disco?). There is some confusion over the names of this and other dances, and different authors adopt different terms. It is therefore necessary to proceed with care when reading about the dance language of bees.

A different kind of vibration

The final means of communication used by bees is *piping*. This is associated with queens, around the time of swarming. Although all the sounds emitted by queen bees are referred to as piping, there are really two different sounds; one made by queens still enclosed in their cells and the other made by queens, both mated and unmated, running free in the hive. The sound is made by the queen pressing her thorax onto the comb, with her wings closed, and vibrating her large flight muscles. Although we can hear the sound that is produced, the bees detect it as vibrations in the comb through their feet. Just another surprising fact of bee life.

The worst enemies of honey
bees are beekeepers!

DEFENDING THE COLONY

A bees' nest is an attractive food opportunity for a great many other animals. All that lovely honey, not to speak of the tasty and nutritious grubs, protein-rich pollen and adult bees, is like a magnet to many different species, large and small. Honey bees have evolved a defence system which is intended to protect their nest and its contents. This does not always work, of course, as some predators have very thick fur or skin which enables them to withstand an attack by bees. Others have become crafty and devised ways to sneak in, but the honey bee colony is remarkably successful at protecting itself especially when we consider the size of the individual insects. In this final section, we see how bees detect potential enemies and how they react to them.

Large predators

In Britain we are lucky because there are comparatively few large predators of honey bee colonies. We have mice, green woodpeckers and, occasionally, badgers, although I have lived with both woodpeckers and badgers and have not had any problems so far. Other animals may have a marginal effect. I have watched a family of baby hedgehogs catching bees returning to mating nuclei in the evening – until one got its nose stung and ran away crying, followed by its brothers and sisters. They did not return. Robins, tits and toads all frequent the apiary but they do not appear to do much damage and, in most cases, probably only pick up dead or dying bees, larvae and pupae. In other parts of the world, bees have much more serious problems and have to contend with a variety of large mammals including honey badgers, skunks and bears. Everywhere, the worst large predators of all are you, me and all our fellow beekeepers.

Wasps can rob a honey bee
colony of its stores in
late summer

Insect enemies

Again, we are fortunate in Britain in only having smallish wasps (although these can do a lot of damage in some cases), little ants and the occasional death's head hawk moth. Other countries have insects, such as army ants, which demolish anything in their path and huge hornets which can pick off large numbers of bees as they return to the nest. In this country, and often in many others, the worst enemy of a hive is another hive whose inhabitants are only too willing to rob the rightful owners of their hard-won stores of honey.

So, how does the honey bee colony recognise these marauders and what does it do about them?

Guards, scent and movement

The entrance to a bee nest is manned by guard bees. They are very alert to movements, particularly rapid ones, in front of the entrance. As beekeepers we know this only too well! Stand in front of a hive and wave your arms about and you will soon be inspected. Depending on the defensive nature of the colony and its condition, you may be merely 'buzzed' or you may be stung. Guards are also receptive to scents. Open a colony when you are sweating profusely or if you have been to the hairdressers and the bees will be far from happy and very soon may start to sting you. Many of our bees in Britain are quite docile but African bees are known to have a short fuse. (You would expect that when you think that they have evolved to deal with a large number of nasty predators compared with our bees.)

Experiments have shown that they react rapidly to carbon dioxide when it is exhaled, so it pays not to breathe all over them. Our bees just move away. Bears, badgers and skunks all have scents which cause defensive behaviour in honey bees. Presumably my baby hedgehogs did too, although their movements at the hive entrance would have contributed to their problems. Once the guard bees have reacted to the sight or smell of an enemy, the colony's defence strategy is deployed.

Honey bees from other colonies are another problem. How do the guard bees distinguish between the bees from their own colony and those from elsewhere? Why do they let some 'foreign' bees in and not others?

Different kinds of intruders

All honey bees have an odour which is colony-specific. This seems to come from the unique mix of nectars that are in the individual hive and are absorbed by the waxy surface of the bee, and from the common crop contents of all the inhabitants of the colony brought about by food sharing (trophallaxis). So, each bee carries around with it a scent identification which can be 'read' by other bees. It is really a bee passport. When a bee tries to enter a hive, a guard bee investigates it with its antennae. It rapidly allows one of its own colleagues in, but its behaviour to strangers will vary because the honey bees which try to go into the 'wrong' hive are of two kinds:

A worker bee in the typical posture of a guard, standing on her back two pairs of legs with the front pair raised

1   Those that accidentally blunder or drift into a hive other than their own.
2   Robbers, who are intentionally trying to gain entry and take away the colony's honey.

These two kinds of bees will behave differently and the guards will react to them differently. Those entering accidentally will probably be bringing a load of nectar with them and will fly straight to the entrance of the colony, attempting to go in as if they belonged there. They have simply made a mistake. The guards will inspect them and, if the incomer is confident, will let her in, although the guard may follow the stranger into the hive, still investigating her. Younger bees, who may be less sure of themselves, are more hesitant. They may stop when inspected and curl up with their legs and abdomen tucked in. This is a submissive posture. They may also release a drop of nectar for the guards to sample and final behaviour is to pull the proboscis through the front feet repeatedly (known as tongue stropping). The guards will usually remove such a bee but without harming her. This is a clear case of 'she who hesitates is lost'. The bold intruder is described as dominant and is usually an older bee who knows the ways of the bee world.

Robbing bees are altogether different. As they approach, they dart about and hover in front of the entrance. They are probably looking for a way to slip in past the guard bees who recognise this behaviour and adopt the characteristic guard bee posture - the front legs raised, mandibles opening and closing. This releases the alarm pheromone, 2-heptanone. We know that this rather weak pheromone repels foraging bees, so it may act as a warning to the robbers and help to drive them away. If they persist and try to enter, the guard bees will challenge them immediately and try to sting them. Fights ensue and there will usually be a number of dead bees in front of a hive which is being targeted by robbers. Other robbers quickly land and, when challenged, run or fly away. They never adopt the submissive posture.

Mobilising reinforcements

Once the guard bees start stinging, the more powerful alarm pheromones are released from the sting chamber. These have a characteristic smell. Many of the books describe it as being like ripe bananas but I perceive it as more like pear drops. (It is a slightly fruity smell and, once you can smell it, it is probably time to close the hive and go home!) Other bees are alerted by it and, immediately, more arrive at the entrance to defend the colony. Whether the intruder is a badger, a bear or another bee, more stings will be deployed. Bees are alerted by the sting pheromone even if there is no actual threat to them. Sometimes the colony will not succeed in saving its precious home and stores and it will be wiped out, but it will not go down without a fight.

Other factors at work

We have seen that two factors are very important in alerting the colony to intruders:

- smell of the predators/robbers
- behaviour of potential intruders.

However, there are other more general influences on defensive behaviour. These are:

- *Time of year*. Colonies are much more defensive during the late summer and early autumn when they have large amounts of stores. In the early part of the year, they are much more relaxed about strange bees and even beekeepers. We all know this from our own experience.
- *Colony conditions*. Small colonies are less likely to attack than large ones. That is one of the reasons for starting novice beekeepers off with a nucleus rather than a huge established colony. A colony which is preparing to swarm or one which has lost its queen may be very easily alerted.

We have all experienced this when we have opened a normally placid colony one day to find it anything but so. There are other circumstances, such as poisoning, which can change the nature of a colony temporarily and make it more defensive.

- *Genetics*. Some bees are simply more defensive than others. This applies particularly to African bees which react more quickly, more aggressively and for longer to potential intruders, but most of us have met colonies which have a very defensive nature. The distance that attacking bees will follow varies enormously, some giving up almost immediately the attacker leaves the vicinity of the nest, others persisting for 100 metres or more. Again, the African races, and particularly Africanised bees, are the worst culprits.

An ongoing problem

Once alerted, a colony remains more defensive for a while. So, if you kick a hive you can probably expect trouble for a time afterwards! Similarly, a colony trying to repel robbing bees or wasps will be sensitive to any interference. The length of time a colony remains on 'full alert' is governed to a large extent by its genetics.

As beekeepers, we encourage 'gentle' bees but, yet again, this may not be the best approach if we look at the honey bee in a purely biological way. A colony which is easily alerted and quick to respond to predators and robbers may be able to protect itself and its valuable stores more successfully and so survive to reproduce. This is an extension of the often-suggested strategy of putting a bad-tempered (ie, very defensive) colony near the gate in apiaries affected by vandalism. Not a good idea in these litigious times, but it illustrates my point!

7 COLONY REPRODUCTION

There is a time of year when bees take to the wing in vast numbers, carrying most of your honey crop with them and annoying the neighbours. It is a time when you get to admire the view from the top of a ladder and hope the telephone will not ring until you have finished lunch. Yes, it's swarming time. Now, you may regard swarms as a nuisance, if you are a beginner you may even dread them, or you might enjoy the spectacle. Whatever your feelings, swarms are a fact of beekeeping life and an integral part of the honey bees' annual cycle.

A colony of honey bees can be called a *super-organism* because each individual bee is only part of the whole and there is only one fully reproductive female. To be successful, in a biological sense, this super-organism needs to reproduce and it does this by swarming. Successful swarming is the establishment of two or more colonies where there was one before and the survival of all those colonies through the winter. The urge to reproduce is very strong in all organisms and that is why swarming is very difficult to stop, but the odd thing is that not all colonies swarm in any one year as you would expect.

A laying queen produces pheromones which are passed all round the colony

THE SWARMING PROCESS

The start — *Lack of pheromones*

What starts the swarming process? The answer is *pheromones*, or rather lack of them. There are two quite distinct pheromones involved:

- *Queen mandibular pheromone* which the queen produces continuously from her mandibular glands and which is spread all over her body. It is distributed by contact

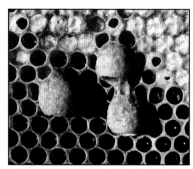

Queen cups are found in all full colonies during the active season

Only a proportion are ever used to raise queens

between bees, starting with the 'court' around the queen. These bees stroke and lick the queen and receive their 'dose' of pheromone. They then move away, contacting other bees who then contact others and so on, so that every bee in the nest receives a small amount of this important messenger. It is possible that there is some spread by food sharing.

- *Queen tarsal pheromone* is produced in the tarsal glands (also called Arnhart's glands after the researcher who first described them) found in the fifth (last) tarsomere of each leg of the queen. It is oily and is left wherever the queen walks over the comb.

It seems that worker bees need a supply of both these pheromones for queen cell production to be suppressed. This is fine but, if the number of bees, particularly young bees, increases to the point where they are severely congested in the brood nest, individuals are not able to move around freely and the pheromones will not be distributed throughout the nest. The inhibition of queen rearing is removed and queen cells are started. As with all things to do with bees, that is not the whole story and a list of other factors involved follows.

- Hereditary factors. Some bees are more 'swarmy' than others.
- Age and condition of queen. Production of pheromones is reduced as a queen ages and there must be some variation in the amount of pheromones that individual queens of the same age produce.
- The external conditions. A *good nectar flow* and *supply of pollen* is essential to build the colony early in the year. Rain may make a colony seem more congested because the foraging bees cannot get out.

Getting ready

Once there are occupied queen cells, these act as a cue which leads to other behaviour:

- the queen is chivvied and jostled by the worker bees
- the queen is slimmed down by a reduction in her food supply so that her egg-laying rate reduces for about a week before the swarm issues
- bees in the brood nest fill their crops with honey
- for about three days before the swarm leaves, some scout bees look for a new home.

A sealed queen cell

A flying swarm is an exciting sight!

Coming out

Swarm issue can be delayed by bad weather, but normally the swarm will come out the day, or day after, the first queen cell is sealed. It starts when some bees do a *'buzzing run'*. This is a dance which involves running rapidly across the comb in a straight line with wings buzzing. The dancing bee crashes into other bees and this starts them off doing buzzing runs themselves. Eventually the whole colony is so disorganised that bees begin to pour out through the entrance. At some stage, the queen is pushed out and the swarm is then airborne. It may contain half or more of the bees from the brood nest and about *70% of the worker bees less than 10 days old* may leave with the swarm. This is very important for swarm establishment because old workers would die before the queen's first brood hatched and began work. A few drones may get caught up in the general excitement but these never amount to more than 1% of the total.

Clustering

After a very short time, the bees begin to gather on a nearby tree, bush, wall or other firm support. (I say 'firm' but I have seen a really stupid swarm clustered on a large dock plant and others in similar places.) Wherever they choose to land, they are attracted there largely by the presence of the queen. From the mandibular glands in her head, she produces a variety of different chemicals. Working in the 1960s, RK Callow identified 13 different chemicals and there were others that he did not identify. I do not include this information to confuse you – as if I would! – but to

**Swarms do not always cluster
on a branch**

indicate that, as usual, we probably do not know the full story because today we are only familiar with two of these chemicals and they play quite different parts in the clustering process.

The pheromone which attracts bees to the cluster is *9-oxodec-2-enoic acid* (9-ODA for short).

Once the queen has settled, this is the chemical which will 'draw in' the flying bees. Many of the worker bees which have landed will also release a pheromone, in this case *Nasonov* pheromone, and this will help in the process.

The second queen pheromone is *9-hydroxydec-2-enoic acid* (9-HDA) and this now comes into play, causing the cluster to stabilise and stay put. It is important to realise that, however much Nasonov pheromone is wafting about, without the two queen pheromones the swarm will return to the hive.

As we know, the bees will stay clustered until 10 minutes before we arrive to capture them. This may be anything from 15 minutes (I don't want to know about the one which sat there for 5 minutes!) to three days. Yes! I have been called out to one which had been there for a week – it went 10 minutes before I arrived. Any small groups of bees that are trying to do their own thing will join the group containing the queen. But during the time the swarm is clustered, some of the bees are very busy.

House hunting

Most of us can empathise with scout bees searching for a new home because we know how it is! You need a new place that's near the shops, not too far from the parents (but not too close), big enough to accommodate the kids as they grow, but small enough to keep warm in the winter, with a sunny aspect and a secure front door – and you have to find space for the big freezer to store all the fruit and vegetables from the garden. Not easy. Now imagine having to satisfy the needs of some 20,000 individuals plus a royal personage in the space of a few hours, a few days at most, and you begin to get a feel for the problems facing a newly emerged swarm of honey bees. At least they do not have to worry about mortgages, deposits and chains!

The ideal home

We can translate the introduction above into the needs of a swarm when choosing a new nest cavity. Experiments to ascertain the precise needs are not always conclusive but, generally, the requirements are as follows:

- a distance of 500–600 metres from the parent colony
- a cavity 40 litres in volume (about the size of a Langstroth brood box)
- a south-facing entrance
- an entrance hole some 35–40 mm in diameter
- an entrance well above ground – probably around 2–3 metres
- the entrance near the bottom of the cavity.

The distance from the parent colony has to be a compromise between reducing competition for forage and the energy needed to travel further. Swarming bees have a finite amount of honey in their crops and this has to last them while they move and set up home.

Size must allow for expansion of the colony and give adequate room for honey storage so that the colony can survive the winter.

A south-facing entrance usually means a warmer and drier home and the size of the entrance is another compromise between ease of access for many foraging bees, ventilation in hot weather, retention of heat in cold weather, exclusion of wind and rain and the ability to defend the entrance against predators. Height of the entrance above ground is also a protection and the entrance position near the bottom of the cavity appears to be the preferred option, although other positions may be accepted.

When a swarm does not successfully relocate to a cavity, it may build a nest in the open where it is clustered

Finding the right place

In our search for the ideal 'Des Res', we probably go to all the Estate Agents in the chosen area and then visit any number of likely homes. Bees don't have estate agents but they do have scouts and the rest of the process is very similar. Scouts investigate likely cavities in the neighbourhood and may begin doing this for about three days before the swarm emerges. (If you see some of your bees investigating roof cavities and similar places round your house, in the summer, it is more than likely that one of your hives is about to swarm – if it has not already done so!)

Reaching a consensus

Once the swarm emerges and clusters, the job of the scouts becomes more urgent. A scout bee finding a suitable cavity will return to the cluster and dance. It will use the waggle dance, executed on the surface of the cluster. No samples will be given (bees don't have Polaroid cameras!) but the dance will demonstrate the distance and direction of the cavity and other bees will then go and investigate it. There may be a number of cavities in the area which are more or less suitable and several different dances may be performed. Gradually, more bees will be recruited to a few sites and eventually virtually all the dances will be directed at one site. At this point, the swarm will take off and relocate to its new home. The whole process may take less than an hour or up to two or three days.

Home selection

So how do the scouts select a new home? Just like us, they look at it carefully and inspect the facilities. A scout bee investigating a potential nest site will crawl round the outside of the site and take short flights to fix its position and view it in relation to its surroundings. She will go inside and crawl round the walls. She will also take short flights inside, between the walls, presumably estimating the size. This is all quite extraordinary behaviour and seems to point to an ability to estimate size and make some sort of assessment. Research work is currently unravelling this complex picture and will soon explain exactly what is going on but, as far as I am concerned, it is a wonderful example of the bees' ability to make important 'decisions'. Scouts may use their Nasonov glands to lay a scent at the cavity entrance and this may help to guide the swarm in, if it eventually chooses this site.

A vital decision

The selection of a new nest site is of paramount importance to a swarm. Upon it rests the future of the colony. Too small or too big, a cold damp location, an entrance which gives easy access to predators, can all spell disaster to the bees as they struggle to establish a new colony and store sufficient honey to last the winter. In the beekeeping situation, we might think about providing a south-facing Langstroth brood box with a reduced entrance, mounted on a pole some 2.5 metres off the ground and at least 500 metres from the next hive as the almost ideal situation, but beekeeping is an artificial situation and we should always keep that in mind.

Moving to the new nest-site

So, a new site has been selected and a consensus has been reached, but how do the bees get there? Remember that the new site may be some distance away, most of the bees in the swarm are young and have probably never been outside the hive before, and bees are not members of the AA or RAC. Movement of the swarm is down to the scout bees. To start the move, bees, probably scouts, start performing buzzing runs on the surface of the swarm and once these spread, so that the cluster is disturbed, the swarm takes to the air. It circles around for a short time and then moves off in the direction of the new site. Only the bees that have visited the site know its position and they guide the swarm in two ways:

- flying backwards and forwards through the swarm
- emitting Nasonov pheromone for the other bees to follow.

The queen is of prime importance. Her pheromones keep the swarm together and, without her, the swarm will break up or return to its old site. In experiments, swarms can be led by queen pheromones alone but can only be led by Nasonov pheromone when a queen is present. This is reasonable when you consider that, without a queen, a new swarm is doomed to failure.

Once the new site is reached, bees start to go in and some fan Nasonov pheromone at the entrance, which has already been marked with this pheromone by the scout bees. Once the queen is inside, the process speeds up and a swarm disappears remarkably quickly into a cavity, fanning bees being the only remaining sign.

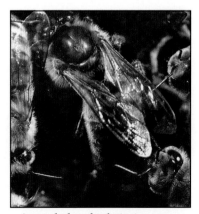

A developing queen pupa

Fate of the original colony

After the prime swarm has departed to pastures new, the original colony has to get itself reorganised. It is now made up of:

- most of the older foraging bees
- some young bees
- a lot of sealed and unsealed brood
- queen cells, sealed and unsealed.

The first queen to emerge, after about a week, may kill all the other queens and take over the colony, or she may fly out with a smaller swarm, usually called a *cast* or afterswarm. Usually there are no more than one or two casts. They may be very small and have no chance of becoming large enough to survive the winter. During this turbulent period in the development of the colony, various forms of communication, which we talked about in Chapter 6, come into operation. Young queens, both in cells and running free in the hive, pipe frequently and workers perform dorso-ventral abdominal vibratory dances on sealed cells and on

A newly hatched virgin queen

young queens. These seem aimed at controlling the emergence of
confined queens, protecting them from the emerged queens and
controlling the young hatched queens. The issue of a cast from
the hive is accompanied by buzzing runs. Eventually, it all settles
down, the new queen mates and begins to lay and the colony gets
back to a stable situation.

Control of the swarming process

The flow chart summarises the methods of communication used
during swarming.

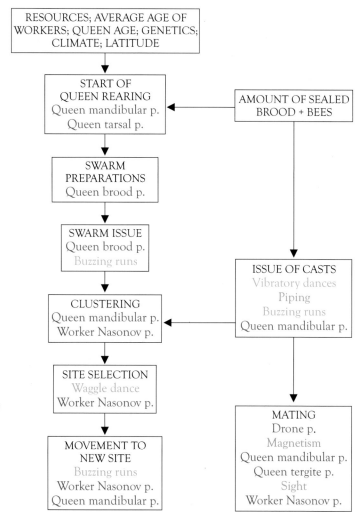

Control of the swarming process

*The flow chart summarises the
methods of communication
used during swarming*

   p = pheromone
  blue = dances
 green = other communication

Addendum

There are always complications and unanswered questions with bee behaviour, and swarming is a prime example.

- Why don't all large colonies swarm each year?
- Why do some colonies produce several casts?
- Why are casts often so skittish?
- Is selection of a nest cavity innate behaviour or is some 'reasoning' involved?

The answer to the first of these questions probably lies in the earlier section dealing with factors affecting the initiation of swarming. The second has been answered, at least partly, by some work done by Mark Winston which showed a direct link between the amount of sealed brood present in the parent colony and the number of casts produced.

This still does not explain why casts are produced when both they and the parent colony may be too small to survive so that, biologically, the whole thing seems unsatisfactory. Perhaps the tropical origins of the honey bee have something to do with it? The question on behaviour of casts is presumably answered to some extent by the presence of an unmated queen. Such queens do not produce as much of the queen pheromones as an older queen and therefore may be less successful at maintaining the integrity of a swarm. That leaves the last question and I think we need to get inside the mind of a bee to answer that!

BUILDING COMB

Once in its new home, the swarm has to sort out the interior. Have you ever employed an interior designer? You probably do what we do and muddle along with MDF from B&Q, paint charts from Homebase and furniture from IKEA! Not so our bees. They have interior design all wrapped up. Having found their cavity (our interior designers would call it 'a space') they fill it full of wax cells. A bit boring perhaps but very practical, especially when you consider that the wax is all made in-house. We looked at wax production in Chapter 2 but now we need to consider how that wax is used to build comb.

An expensive commodity

It may be made in-house, but beeswax does not come cheap. It needs a large amount of sugar (from honey or nectar) to produce wax. The actual amount is a somewhat flexible measurement, varying between 4 kg and 16 kg of honey per 1 kg of wax depending on which book you read. I think a figure of 6–8 kg would be a reasonable one to work with. Then there is the need for the bee producing the wax to have eaten large amounts of pollen. This will be necessary for the production of well-developed wax glands. So, wax production represents quite a drain on colony resources and new comb is built only when needed. The most obvious time is when a swarm is establishing itself in a new cavity. Otherwise, comb is constructed when there are large quantities of incoming nectar and no space to store it.

Heat and co-operation

To produce wax in quantity, a temperature of 35 °C has to be maintained. The secreting bees must be well fed (the best ones are those 10–18 days old). The bees which left with a prime swarm will have crops full of nectar and, as they are mostly young bees, they will have eaten large quantities of pollen. In established colonies, there must be a good flow of incoming nectar. The bees hang together in chains and tiny transparent scales of beeswax exude from the wax glands. The bee picks these up with the pollen brushes on the inside of her hind legs and transfers them to the front legs where they are moistened with saliva and kneaded, by the front legs and the mandibles, to make them pliable. The bee then adds the softened wax to the work of the other bees and it becomes part of the comb.

That sounds easy. But if you consider that there will be a large number of bees involved, each contributing their own bit of wax, that they have no tools other than their own bodies, that it is dark and that the cell size must be precise, the process becomes another miracle of bee life.

Hairy plumb-bobs and inbuilt callipers

Within the nest, the comb is used for rearing young and for storing liquid and solid food. Space must be used efficiently and house bees must be able to move freely and quickly between different parts. Therefore the main requirements when constructing comb are:

- the sheets of comb must hang vertically
- the combs must be parallel to one another
- there must be adequate, but not excess, space between adjacent combs
- the cells must be the correct size.

Now honey bees do not run around with a little bit of lead on a string, so they need some sort of structure to do the work of a plumb-bob. This will enable the comb to be built vertically and not at odd angles. It has to be fixed to the top surface of the cavity and not to the sides or floor so the bee needs to know which way is up.

To solve these problems, the bee has hairs collected together and mounted on hard plates which are part of the cuticle. These *hair plates* are found where there is movement between parts of the bee around the thorax and, from the point of view of comb building, the most important ones seem to be where the head meets the thorax. The hairs are connected to nerves and when the position of the bee changes, relative to gravity, the head and thorax will change position slightly, the hairs will be bent differently, the nerves will be stimulated and send impulses to the central nervous system which interprets them as the bee's orientation in space.

So, the individual bee can 'know' when it is horizontal, when vertical and when at an angle relative to gravity. Incidentally, if these hairs are removed, the bee is completely unable to build comb. Other hair plates are found in the petiole (waist), where the legs join the thorax, and between the first two segments of the legs (coxae and trochanters), but these do not seem as important in comb building as the ones in the neck. (In a totally different context, this ability to know up, down and angles is very important when a bee is performing the waggle dance.)

Measurement in comb building is fascinating. Cells have a fairly constant diameter, although there is some variation between races and strains of bee, the thickness of the walls is constant and the angles within the cells are all 120°. Worker cells are about 5 mm and drone cells 6 mm in diameter.

How do they know? They probably use their front legs as callipers for measuring cell diameter but it is impossible to test this experimentally as they need their front legs for the manipulation of the wax in the first place. Sense organs in the tips of the antennae detect the thickness of the walls. The distance between the centre of one comb and the next is 3.5 cm, but how they work out the position of the next comb is still a mystery.

Firm foundations and a perfect structure (almost)

All of us who have kept a captured swarm in a box for a few hours have seen the beginning of comb-building. When we look at the top of the box, we find patches of wax, sometimes quite thick, and even a small piece of comb hanging down. The bees start by depositing several layers of wax on the roof of the box (or any

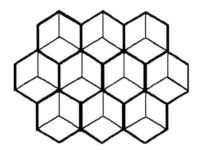

The perfect interlocking structure

other cavity). These foundations must be strong because, eventually, the comb may be very big and heavy. When the accumulation of wax is quite thick, the bees start drawing some of it out into cells which may at first be shallow and not fully formed. These become part of the foundations, but then the cells take their proper shape with individual bees adding bits of wax or shaping and thinning the walls until they are the right shape and size.

I must mention, at this point, something you all know – the cells of honeycomb are hexagonal, with a point usually at the bottom. This is not unusual because other social insects, such as wasps, use the same shape, although wasps actually build their combs horizontally. The hexagon is the most efficient shape in terms of material used in construction and number of cells per unit area. The beeswax cells are built at an angle of about 13° to the horizontal and this prevents the liquid nectar running out. They are also built back to back and the two opposite rows of cells are staggered, so that the side walls of one help to strengthen the opposite one – difficult to describe but the little diagram should help.

There are a few problems in this apparently perfect exercise. The bees often start their construction in several places and then join up the individual pieces of work – a bit like patchwork. Where the separate pieces join, there may be cells with strange shapes and sizes to make it all fit together. Also, over time, the load which the comb carries can cause the cells to distort so that they are not all a perfect shape. Finally, cross-bridges have to be built to help strengthen and support big combs.

A multipurpose interior

Comb, once built, can be used over and over again for many years. Admittedly, it changes from the beautiful pristine white comb which the swarm constructs to old black comb, due to the passage of millions of tiny feet, the addition of propolis and the accumulation of cocoons, but during its period of use it can function as nursery, kitchen, pantry, resting place, dance floor and general living space. It can be taken out of service or extended, as need dictates. It is manufactured from in-house materials using built-in tools. Like all interior design, it comes at a cost, but this is strictly regulated by the available income of the community and, unlike human interior design, expenditure never exceeds resources.

8 INSIDE AND OUTSIDE INFLUENCES

In this final chapter, we need to think about the way that the honey bee colony is affected by the environment outside the nest and by changes inside the nest. The two are very closely related in many ways. We will begin by considering the annual pattern to colony life and the effects of seasonal changes. The second part of the chapter will look at the substances honey bees collect from the outside world.

A YEAR IN THE LIFE OF A HONEY BEE COLONY

A colony of honey bees can survive for ever – in theory. It is, therefore, referred to as a perennial colony, but it does have an annual cycle of development.

Put very simply, in a temperate country such as Britain, the colony starts to expand, slowly at first in the very early part of the year and then more rapidly, until it is big enough to swarm. It then splits itself into two (or three or four) colonies, each of which have to work their socks off so that they get in enough food to survive the winter when there are no flowers about and the temperatures are low.

Having stored sufficient honey for their needs, the colony then winds down to the winter, which it spends feeding on the stored food and keeping warm enough to survive. That is only an outline and we need to look much more closely at what goes on at each stage of the year.

I propose to start the story in the middle of winter, when the calendar year starts, but we should remember that for us beekeepers, the year really starts in early autumn when we prepare our colonies for the winter.

In early spring, honey bee colonies start to expand

Winter aconites
(*Eranthis hyemalis*) **can provide
a source of nectar and pollen
in late winter**

Winter into spring

At the turn of the year, when you are still recovering from the excesses of Christmas eating and too many late nights, the bees are inside their hives almost ready to start their preparations for summer and those short months of frenetic activity. Their main requirement at this time is to keep warm enough to prevent death.

As the temperature drops, the bees gather together and eventually form a cluster. Within the cluster, the bees slowly consume food so that heat can be produced and conserved, maintaining the bees at a high enough temperature to keep them alive. The minimum temperature for the survival of the individual bee is 8 °C but the centre of the cluster will be much higher than this, probably around at least 20 °C. As the *external* (outside or ambient) temperature fluctuates, the cluster loosens or tightens and the more activity there is in the hive, the more food is needed.

It is in the midst of this survival period, in late January or early February, that the queen lays the first eggs of the season. At first she does not lay many and they have to be kept at about 34.5 °C. To maintain this temperature, the colony must produce more heat and consume more food, but it is the first stage in the enormous build-up of the colony which will culminate in swarming. At this point, the bees will number 10,000–15,000.

Spring expansion

You may start to think about looking at your bees and putting on the first super in March or April, but the bees are already well on their way by this time with the queen laying merrily and numbers of young bees increasing. The queen's egg-laying rate is governed by the amount of food she receives and this has been increased as the days lengthen and more forage, particularly pollen, becomes available. She reaches a peak, probably in mid-to-late May, when she can lay as many as 1500 or more eggs per day for a short period and the colony is really expanding fast.

However, in March, the bees are certainly not out of the wood and this is when many colonies die. The brood is increasing, new bees are hatching, the old, overwintered bees are dying and stores are getting low. If the population falls too low, if stores run out before there is much forage about, or if the weather keeps bees in the hive, disaster can strike. Get them past March and things should look up!

In April, the first drone eggs are laid. Drones are related to all the workers in the colony and, although their production uses up valuable colony reserves, they are important because they pass on the colony's genes. Their production is programmed to coincide with swarming so that they will be available to mate with as many queens as possible from the colonies in the area.

The exciting bit – early summer

By May or June, the colony is still building up and it probably contains between 30,000 and 40,000 bees with lots of developing brood from the peak in egg-laying. In particular, there will be a great deal of sealed brood and this is vital to the next stage in the colony's development. So what does it do? It swarms. We are not going into that here because it has already been discussed in detail in Chapter 7, but we need to mention egg production.

Before she leaves with a swarm, the queen is put on a weight-reduction diet so that she is slim enough to fly. Because of this, her egg-laying rate drops markedly about a week before swarming. Prior to this, she is well fed and lays at a high rate. With the swarm and the queen gone, taking quite a bit of food with them, the colony is at a very critical point. If a new queen is not hatched and mated successfully it will, as Private Fraser used to say, be doomed. There is no new brood produced during this period so that future population growth is compromised. The hatching brood will start to replace the bees which have left but, if casts (afterswarms) leave, many of these newly hatched bees will go with them, further reducing the population.

Once a new queen takes over the colony and starts to lay eggs, the immediate crisis is over and the colony begins to rebuild. The priority now, for both this colony and its daughter swarm(s), is to gather sufficient food to survive the winter and to build up the numbers of bees so that they can repeat the whole exercise next year. The queens will have to be well fed to enable them to lay a great number of eggs.

In the colony which does not swarm (and believe it or not, some of them don't!) the uninterrupted period during summer leads to very large populations, strong overwintering colonies and the ability to gather large food reserves for the winter but, although we may appreciate this and regard them as successful colonies, from the biological point of view they have failed because they have not reproduced.

Summer into autumn

As days grow shorter and cooler and food is in shorter supply, the bees begin to batten down the hatches for winter. Where the queen is a new one, she will carry on laying eggs into late October

Colonies build up rapidly on oilseed rape during early summer

Ivy is the last major nectar producer in autumn

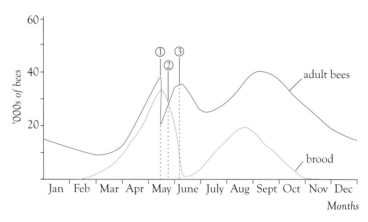

Annual variation in brood and adult bee numbers in a colony of honey bees

①= issue of swarm
②= new queen hatches
③= new queen starts laying

or November but, if she is old, she may stop completely in September or early October. Late crops, such as ivy, are still collected but the winter cluster begins to form with the onset of colder nights. The young worker bees now hatching will have to survive for up to six months (compared with their summer sisters, who live for five or six weeks only), so they eat large quantities of pollen to build up their body reserves. The annual cycle has come to an end.

Changes ahead?

Changes that are going on in the environment are likely to affect this pattern of bee behaviour. No one quite knows how, so this conclusion is a collection of questions (I am never short of unanswered questions!).

The higher temperatures which we are experiencing cause the queens to continue laying for longer in the autumn and start earlier in the spring. Will this trend continue? Will we get to the stage where there is no brood break at all? What significance will this have for new pests? Earlier forage, particularly oilseed rape, will result in rapid early build-up. So will swarming preparations get earlier? Will April become the prime month for swarms? Will global warming result in more rain during the summer, as has been predicted? What will that do to our early, big colonies? Will there be sufficient sunny days for them to take advantage of the huge nectar crops produced by well-watered plants, or will they be shut in their hives for long periods, making queen cells and passing diseases around?

Lots of questions, all without immediate answers.

KEEPING COOL AND KEEPING WARM

Temperature is very important to all living organisms. All birds and mammals are able to keep their internal temperature constant whatever the outside (ambient) temperature. They are said to be *homoiothermic* (warm-blooded). In all other animals, including the insects, the internal temperature varies with the ambient temperature and they are said to be *poikilothermic*. (They are sometimes described as 'cold-blooded' but this is a complete misnomer because they may be hot or cold and some of the simpler animals do not even have blood!)

Why is internal body temperature so important? Within any animal there are many chemical reactions going on all the time. Collectively, these are called metabolism and each reaction needs its own enzyme. Enzymes all have an optimal temperature at which they work best (usually between 30 °C and 40 °C) so maintaining metabolism at a constant rate requires a constant internal body temperature. If a poikilothermic animal cools down, because the ambient temperature is low, its metabolism will slow down and, if it warms up because the ambient temperature is high, its metabolism will speed up. The animal will die if its metabolism becomes too slow or too fast.

Heat production and heat loss

In any animal, heat is produced as a by-product of the metabolic processes and by muscle activity. It is lost by evaporation of water from various parts, particularly any openings such as spiracles, and by convection from the surface of the animal. However, the losses by both these methods will depend on other external conditions. So, for example, in humid conditions evaporation will be reduced and where there is a breeze, convection and evaporation will be increased. Because a bee is small, its surface area is high in relation to its volume and this will increase its heat loss, but its hairy covering will help to insulate it and trap a layer of warm, still air next to the cuticle. When it is in the sun, it will absorb heat and a darker coloured bee will absorb more heat than a lighter coloured one. This is probably why bumblebees and our native honey bees are dark: they are adapted to temperate conditions where the ambient temperature is often low.

Resting and flying

A bee resting in warm conditions will have no temperature problems because its heat production will be balanced by its heat

As temperatures rise, bees spread out on the combs and some may move outside the hive

loss, but flying is a very energetic occupation. The huge flight muscles, which occupy most of the thorax, generate a great deal of heat during flight. This can lead to overheating and, to offset this, the breathing rate increases so that more water is evaporated from the spiracles.

There is also a very clever heat exchange mechanism which comes into play. If you look at the circulatory system of the honey bee you will see that the aorta leads from the heart and passes through the petiole (waist) and the thorax. As it goes through the thorax, the haemolymph absorbs heat from the flight muscles and much of this will be lost in the head and, later, in the gaster (abdomen minus A1) as the haemolymph circulates.

The gaster is effectively separate from the thorax and is always cooler. It is also less well insulated so heat is lost more readily. As the internal temperature of the thorax rises, the heart rate increases so that the haemolymph is pumped round at a greater rate. A foraging bee can increase heat loss by regurgitating a drop of nectar from its crop and allowing this to evaporate, so removing heat from the head. A bee can also move into the shade if it is starting to overheat in the sun.

When a bee's internal temperature starts to cool below the optimum, it can generate heat by vibrating its big flight muscles and it is able to do this even when it is resting. So, the individual bee is able to control its temperature to some extent but would not be able to maintain a constant temperature in extremes of ambient temperatures.

The colony situation

So far, we have looked at the individual bee, but bees function at two levels – individual and colony. In each case, the broad principles of temperature control (thermoregulation) remain the same.

As we have already seen, the broodnest must be maintained at around 34.5 °C. It can vary a little, but wide fluctuations will damage the brood for the same reasons that wide fluctuations cause problems in the adult bee. Worker bees have a small number of sensilla on each antenna which detect temperature (and humidity) changes.

We will look first at the problems of overheating. Believe it or not, this can occur during our British summer when temperatures start to soar and it is even more of a problem in hotter parts of the world. There are various ways in which the bees can keep the temperature of the hive stable:

- they spread out on the combs and some may hang outside to create more space.

During cold winter weather
the bees cluster together
inside the hive

- bees fan their wings, some at the entrance and some on the combs. This causes a more rapid circulation of air and the removal of warm air.
- some bees regurgitate water, or nectar, on the surface of sealed brood or on the walls of open cells. These drops of water may be spread into a thin sheet by the bee repeatedly beating them with her tongue, a process called tongue-lashing. Evaporation of this liquid cools down the hive.

These various cooling processes kick in when the nest temperature rises towards 36 °C. Normally, only a small percentage of bees collect water and some of these may specialise in this activity. When there is danger of overheating, other bees are recruited to fetch water by the receiving bees, which unload the foragers bringing in water or thin nectar much more quickly than those carrying nectar with a high sugar content.

When the weather starts to turn cold, the bees have to adopt a different strategy. At about 18 °C they begin to huddle together in little groups and, as the temperature falls, a single cluster is formed which gradually gets tighter until, at 0 °C, it is as tight as it ever gets. A tight cluster has an inner core where the bees can move about a little and an outer, insulating shell of inactive bees. The bees in the centre of the cluster change places with the ones on the outside from time to time but even so, in a very cold period, many bees will die. Eight degrees Celsius is the lower lethal temperature for a honey bee and, once it gets down to this, it will die, perhaps not immediately, but soon afterwards. To keep the temperature up in the centre of the cluster, the bees vibrate their flight muscles, generating heat just as the individual bee does. Muscle use requires energy and this comes from the honey, which the bees gradually consume. During the winter, a colony will use an average of about 1 kg per week, just for heat production, so do not skimp on feeding! If the colony is broodless, the temperature in the middle of the cluster is probably kept to around 20 °C. When brood rearing starts and the bees have to raise the temperature, there is some assistance from the brood because older larvae and pupae also generate heat.

Individual or colony?

Temperature of both the individual bee and the colony is controlled by the generation of heat using the flight muscles and the evaporation of water/nectar. Within the colony, the ratio of surface area to volume is also adjusted, by dispersing when hot and clustering when cold. Individual bees do not go around fanning themselves but, collectively, they can produce cooling air currents through the hive. You can help your bees by careful hive positioning to take advantage of winter sunshine, protecting hives from prevailing winds, perhaps providing shade during the hottest part of the year and ensuring the colonies have adequate winter stores and a readily available supply of water but, apart from knitting them all little jumpers for Christmas, there is not a lot more you can do.

WORKER BEES IN WINTER AND SUMMER

From the beekeeper's point of view, the difference between summer worker bees and winter worker bees is that those living during the summer have a short life of about five weeks while those emerging in August, September and later survive during the whole winter, not dying until early spring when new bees are hatching to take their place. The longevity of these winter bees is critical to the success of the colony. Those colonies going into winter with a large number of healthy adult bees stand a much better chance of being successful in the following season.

So, why do these winter bees live longer? There are four reasons:

- their bodies contain large amounts of stored glycogen, protein and fat in the fat bodies
- their hypopharyngeal glands are plump and full of brood food
- their metabolic rate is lower than in summer bees
- they do very little work .

Food use is the key

All worker bees eat large quantities of pollen in the days following their emergence from the cell. During the active season, the protein from the pollen is converted into brood food in the hypopharyngeal glands and this is fed to the larvae. However, bees hatching later in the year have very little, or no brood to feed so the hypopharyngeal glands remain plump and full. Some of the surplus protein is diverted into the fat bodies. The bees also eat large quantities of nectar or honey which helps to build up the fat bodies.

These two factors seem to be the main triggers to the increased lifespan. Abundant supplies of nectar/honey and, particularly, pollen are essential to the survival of the winter bees. It is interesting to see from experimental work that removing all brood from nurse bees in the summer, so maintaining their hypopharyngeal glands and fat bodies in a plump condition, extends the life of those bees.

The lower metabolic rate, resulting in a general slowing down, and the reduction in the amount of work, both inside and outside the colony, means that these winter bees have an easy time of it compared with their summer sisters. Of course, once brood starts to increase in early spring, these old bees have to work hard and their hypopharyngeal glands and fat bodies soon become depleted, the protein being passed on to the developing larvae. Some become foragers on the early crops such as sallow and crocuses and they are soon worn out and die, but not before they have helped to kick-start the colony into its spring expansion.

A honey bee on borage
(*Borago officinalis*)

Bees are able to select the most economic nectar sources

PROVISIONS

We have seen how the external environment affects the life of the colony of honey bees but it also provides the raw materials for its existence. Bees collect four substances:

- nectar
- water
- pollen
- propolis.

We probably all know that. But how do they collect them and what do they do with them? The first two are liquids, so we will deal with those first.

Nectar

This is the bees' basic energy food and the average colony needs 120 kg of nectar per year. The foraging bees collect it from flowers (and sometimes from elsewhere), using their probosces to get it from the flowers' nectaries and into their crops. Carrying back nectar with a high sugar content is more efficient than carrying a watery nectar. Bees are able to distinguish between different sugar concentrations and, using the dance language, the colony will be directed to flowers producing sugar-rich nectar, providing that there are adequate numbers and they are close together.

Foraging bees need a great deal of energy for flying so they also

An oilseed rape flower
(*Brassica napus*)

Three of the nectaries can be seen, each exuding a drop of nectar

eat some nectar themselves, passing it through the proventriculus and into the ventriculus. The crop (honey stomach) is an elastic bag which can hold a maximum of around 100 mg, but the individual bee usually carries about 40 mg of nectar back to the nest on each trip. This should not be construed as laziness but is probably behaviour which takes into account the distance from the nest and the time spent collecting. After all, I can carry a 25 kg bag of corn but I do not expect to lug that weight of shopping back from the greengrocers in one trip! The bee will visit many flowers, usually of the same type, until it has a load of nectar and it may have to learn how the flower works to reach the food.

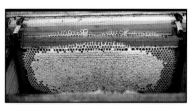

Honey is sealed over with wax once it has reached a moisture content of about 18%. It will keep for a long time

What happens to the nectar after the foraging bee returns to the nest? She gives it to one or more house bees (called 'receiver bees') by regurgitating it onto the proboscis. The receiver bee takes it with her proboscis, carries it away and puts it into a cell in the food storage area of the nest. Alternatively, a receiver bee may need some food and may consume all or part of the nectar she receives. Other bees may also eat some of the nectar or use it to feed older larvae. Any surplus will be processed into honey, a gradual process during which some more of the nectar may be eaten. During processing, quite large amounts of water will be evaporated from the nectar (which may contain anything up to 70% water) and this water will initially go into the nest and help to keep the humidity high. The humidity inside the nest is normally 40–50% and any major deviation from these levels will harm the developing brood. So, nectar is either eaten by adult bees or older larvae or converted into honey and stored.

Processing and storage of honey

Honey bees make honey! 'That's a bit obvious,' I hear you say, but the questions we have to ask are why and how? We can answer the first of these questions simply:

- honey bees have large, perennial colonies containing many adult and immature individuals
- they feed entirely on nectar and pollen from flowers
- flowers do not bloom in sufficient numbers throughout the whole year
- a food store is essential to protect against shortages, even in tropical countries
- in temperate regions a large amount of food is needed to survive the winter
- the food must be in a form which will not deteriorate over several months.

The 'how' of honey production is not quite as simple. The raw nectar must be changed into honey. It will contain 20–70% water and various sugars, mainly sucrose, glucose and fructose, in differing proportions depending on the source of the nectar. If stored in this form, the high concentration of water and the presence of natural yeasts and bacteria would cause the nectar to ferment and grow moulds. There are two principal changes which take place:

- *evaporation of water* to reduce the content to 17–18%
- *chemical changes* due to addition of enzymes.

Water is evaporated by the action of the house bees. A bee takes a drop of nectar onto its partly folded proboscis, so exposing it to the air in the nest. This is done repeatedly. Other house bees fan at the entrance, causing a current of air to pass through the nest and evaporate water from the exposed drops and the surface of nectar in the open cells. During a good nectar flow, an enormous amount of work is done to evaporate huge amounts of water.

The chemical changes are due principally to two enzymes:

1 *Invertase* is added by the bee which collects the nectar. It is produced in its hypopharyngeal glands and splits each molecule of sucrose into two smaller molecules, one of glucose and one of fructose. More invertase is probably added by the house bees.
2 *Glucose oxidase* also comes from the hypopharyngeal gland and acts on glucose, breaking some of it down to give gluconic acid and hydrogen peroxide. The hydrogen peroxide is particularly important as it destroys bacteria.

When the water content has been reduced sufficiently, the bees seal over the honey with wax cappings and it will then keep for a very long time. Bacteria and yeasts are unable to grow because of the high concentration of sugar, the antibacterial activity of the hydrogen peroxide and the exclusion of air and water.

A perfect food store

With the honey stowed away safely, the bees have a good food store to last them over dearth periods when little or no nectar is available. The simple sugars are very easily digested and, by diluting the honey with water, a ready food is available for adults and young. Then some big greedy biped comes along and steals it all – but that's another story!

Water

That brings us to our second fluid – water. Water is often needed to dilute stores or to dissolve the sugars in granulated honey. But it has other uses too. Nurse bees need a great deal of water, because the brood food fed to young larvae (up to four days) is 70–80% water. A further use for water is as a cooling agent when the nest risks overheating during periods of hot weather.

We know that a lot of nectar is rather 'watery', so nectar provides a supply of water for the individual bees' needs as they eat it. The water evaporated from nectar during honey production passes into the hive atmosphere, so this helps to cool the hive and to keep its humidity high, but there are some circumstances where extra water is needed and this is brought back to the nest from nearby water sources by foraging bees. They carry it in their crops in exactly the same way as they would carry nectar. Water collection is particularly noticeable at the following times:

Honey bees collect water from a duckweed-covered pond in early spring

- late winter when stores need dilution and/or dissolving
- early spring when nurse bees need water for brood food production in an expanding brood nest, particularly when the weather is cold or wet
- very hot weather when water is needed to cool down the nest.

It is important to realise that water is always available if the bees need it, so normally only a few foragers will collect water when required. They tend to be a small specialist group, but when there is a demand for larger quantities of water, other bees are recruited by dancing and then the number of water carriers increases dramatically. To maximise collection of water, bees always collect it fairly close to the nest, so reducing travelling time and increasing the number of loads they can carry per day.

The other interesting fact is that nectar collection does not diminish as water collection increases. In fact, it can increase, and it is thought that a separate group of workers, drawn from bees doing nothing within the colony (resting), is recruited to collect and receive the water.

The fluid economy of a colony

Nectar, honey and water cannot be considered as separate commodities in the economy of the honey bee colony. They are all part of the same picture. The diagram I have devised (overleaf) summarises the relationships between these three fluids.

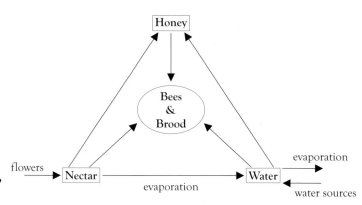

The relationship between nectar, honey and water

Pollen

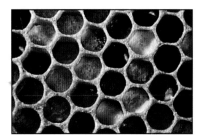

Pollen stored in cells

Pollen loads collected from the bottom of a hive. There is great variation in colour

In Chapter 1, we saw how the worker honey bee collects and carries pollen back to the colony. Once there, it is packed firmly into cells and the bees add various substances, including enzymes, which prevent its germination and inhibit growth of moulds. It is estimated that the average colony needs 20 kg of pollen per year. 125 mg is needed for each larva reared and the average pollen load of a returning forager is 15 mg, although this can be very variable. You only have to watch bees bringing in pollen to see that some have bulging pollen baskets while others carry only small loads.

Now, I am no mathematician, but the work involved in bringing home all that pollen, plus the nectar we have already discussed, and some water, is extraordinary. In any normal colony, there is some stored pollen, usually just above the brood nest, and this is maintained at a fairly constant 1 kg. This provides a cushion against short periods when the foragers are unable to go out.

Why is pollen so important? It is produced by the anthers of flowers and contains the male nuclei which the plant needs to fertilise its eggs but, to the bee, it is the source of protein, vitamins, minerals and lipids (fats).

The young bees need all of these, particularly protein, for the development of the glandular system, and the larvae need it for their growth and development. Up to about 10 days old, young bees eat large quantities of pollen. Amino acids are the building blocks of proteins. They are simpler substances which are fastened together into chains to make individual proteins. The molecule of a specific protein may be very big (for a molecule!) and may be folded and joined in various ways.

When protein-breaking enzymes, called proteases, act on the protein molecule, they break it into its constituent amino acids. These are then used to build new protein. So, in our young bee, pollen proteins are broken down into their amino acids in the ventriculus, the amino acids are carried in the haemolymph to the brood food glands and here they are rebuilt, in different combinations and sequences, into brood food.

There are more than 20 amino acids, but honey bees need only 10 of them. Different pollens contain different amino acids, so a range of pollens is necessary for proper colony growth and it is always noticeable that, even when bees are situated on a very productive crop such as oilseed rape, some will collect pollen from the weeds within that crop and from other plants nearby, even though the majority will be collecting pollen from the rape flowers.

The anthers of *Salix caprea* are a rich source of early pollen

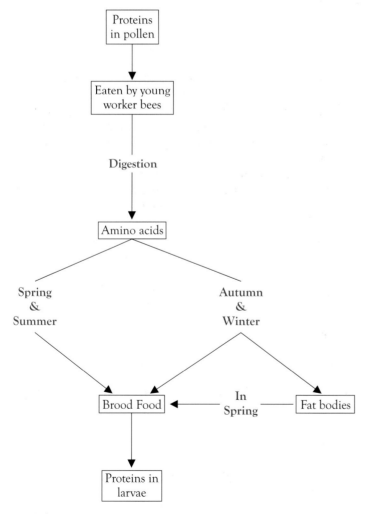

The use of pollen in the colony
(simplified diagram)

A forager enters a hive carrying a load of propolis

Propolis can be used to reduce the size of the hive entrance

A death's head hawk moth which has been completely propolised inside a hive

(Notice the difference in size between the moth and the bee)

Propolis

We all know propolis as that sticky stuff that gets all over our hands and, worse, our clothes when we handle any hive parts, but to the bees it is the fourth vital commodity that they have to import. They get it from tree buds and conifers. In our garden, which contains several pine trees, I often watch the bees scraping the resin from the branches with their mandibles. Because it comes from many different sources, it varies in colour, through various brown and reddish shades, and composition. It is carried back to the hive in the corbiculae, being passed from the mandibles to the front legs, then the middle legs and finally to the hind legs on the same side (pollen is passed to the corbicula on the opposite side). When the bee gets back to the hive with its little globules of glistening propolis, it cannot remove them from its legs so another worker chews them off and uses them immediately.

So why do bees collect propolis, other than to make our lives more difficult? They use it in a variety of ways:

- it fills up small cracks, keeping out draughts and rain and helping to deter wax moth
- in the wild it is used to varnish the inside of the selected cavity
- it is used for varnishing all the cells before the queen lays in them. Its antiseptic qualities help to ensure healthy brood
- sometimes it is built into walls at the front of the hive to reduce the entrance, both for defence and to protect against bad weather
- it is used in comb foundations to strengthen and cement them
- any large intruders, such as mice or slugs, which enter the hive and either die or are killed by the bees but are too big to remove, are covered in propolis so that they do not decay and pollute the nest.

The antiseptic qualities of propolis are extremely important to the honey bee colony and are probably the main reason why the bees collect it. Even we humans have found it useful in the past and it is now enjoying a revival as recent research has shown its value in some areas of medicine.

APPENDIX
UNDERSTANDING THE JARGON

When I first started writing articles about honey bee biology, one of my readers wrote to me to suggest that, because he had no scientific background, he found a certain amount of difficulty knowing how to pronounce some of the words I used and he needed some help. I have attempted to do this in the Glossary on page 141 but his letter set me thinking about scientific terminology in general and the difficulties which can be experienced sometimes, so I am going to lay down a few ground rules which I hope may help a little.

Latin or Greek?

Many scientific terms are filched from Latin or Greek and their endings present problems when we try to put them into the plural. The basic rules are:

Singular	Plural
-us	-i
-a	-ae (ee or ie as in tie)
-um	-a
-is	-es (-ees)
-on	-a

The first three of these are Latin and the second two are Greek. Examples are as follows:

Singular	Plural
ocellus	ocelli
maxilla	maxillae
ommatidium	ommatidia
ecdysis	ecdyses
pleuron	pleura

Simple, isn't it? There are things sent to confuse, such as the word 'corpus' which in the plural becomes 'corpora', so one corpus allatum becomes two corpora allata, and 'genus' which becomes 'genera'.

Some knowledge of Latin and Greek vocabulary is useful. Some words occur frequently. For example 'ad' is Latin for 'to' and 'e' or 'ex' means 'from'. The verb 'fero' means 'I carry'. From these we get the terms afferent and efferent. So, an afferent nerve is one carrying an impulse towards the central nervous system (CNS) and an efferent nerve carries impulses away from the CNS.

The ancient Romans called honey 'mel', so the scientific name for our honey bee, *Apis mellifera*, literally means the bee which carries honey, which is not a strictly accurate description!

What's in a name?

Mention of *Apis mellifera* brings us to the question of scientific names.

All organisms have a two-part scientific name, a system introduced by Linnaeus in the mid-eighteenth century. The first is the name of the genus to which the animal/ plant belongs. It is always given a capital letter and, where the genus is obvious, it may be abbreviated just to this capital letter.

A genus is a group of animals or plants which are very closely related and may be so similar as to be virtually indistinguishable from one another to the casual observer.

However, the members of a genus cannot normally interbreed. An example is the genus *Bombus* which includes the social bumblebees.

The second name is the name of the species (sometimes abbreviated to sp. or spp. if it is plural) to which the organism belongs and is always given a lower-case letter. All members of a species are able to interbreed. So, *Bombus lapidarius*, the large red-tailed bumblebee is a species of bumblebee. All the insects belonging to that species will be able to breed with one another to produce more red-tailed bumblebees, but they will not be able to breed with members of the species *B.terrestris*, the buff-tailed bumblebee.

Scientists use scientific names because they are the only method of ensuring that they are all talking about the same organism and they know for certain which organism it is! Using common names would lead to all sorts of confusion as some animals and plants have a number of common names, many of them very local.

Within a particular species, recognisable groups may develop, due usually to geographical separation by features such as mountain ranges or seas. Such groups may be referred to as sub-species and given a third name which follows the first two. So we have *Apis mellifera mellifera* and *Apis mellifera carnica*. Eventually, sub-species may evolve so many different characteristics that they become separate species.

One final point – when scientific names are written, they are either put into italics or underlined, so that the name of the bee louse will be written *Braula coeca* or Braula coeca (*Bror*-la or *Brow*-la *see*-ka) or abbreviated to *B.coeca* where the genus is known, but beware using the abbreviated form unless you have previously used the full name.

GLOSSARY

In this glossary, I have attempted to give guidance on pronunciation of some words by putting phonetic spelling in brackets. The accented syllable is in *italics*. There are often alternative ways of pronouncing words. Note that the definitions relate to the honey bee and that words may have wider or different meanings in other branches of biology.

age polyethism (age pol-ee-*eeth*-ism)
Change in activities of the worker honey bee, related to age.

allelomorph (al-*eel*-oh-morf)
One of a pair or series of genes found at the same locus on homologous chromosomes.

amino acid
Structural unit containing the amino group (–NH$_2$) and from which proteins are built.

anterior
Front. cf. posterior.

aorta (ai-*yor*-ta)
Blood vessel, a forward continuation of the heart.

apodeme (*a*-poh-deem)
Extension of the cuticle on the inside of the body wall to give attachment for muscles.

arolium (a-*roll*-eeum)
Central part of the foot used as a suction pad.

Arthropoda
Large division (phylum) of the animal kingdom containing the insects and other groups.

basitarsus (bay-zi-*tar*-sus)
Proximal section of the tarsus.

chemoreceptor (*keem*-oh-ree-sept-or)
Sense organ stimulated by a chemical.

chitin (*kie*-tin)
A complex fibrous substance, giving strength and flexibility, found in part of the cuticle.

chorion (*kor*-ree-on)
The outer covering of the egg.

chromosome
Thread-shaped structure in the nucleus of every cell. Visible during cell division.

cibarium (sigh-*bear*-ree-um)
First part of the oral cavity of the honey bee.

corbicula (kor-*bik*-you-la)
The pollen basket.

corpus allatum (*kor*-pus al-*ait*-um)
One of a pair of endocrine glands producing juvenile hormone.

corpus cardiacum (*kor*-pus kar-*dee*-ak-um)
One of a pair of endocrine glands.

cuticle
Outer covering of the larva, pupa and adult honey bee.

deutocerebrum (dyoot-oh-se-*reeb*-rum)
Part of the brain derived from the middle portion of the embryo brain.

diploid
Having a double set of paired (homologous) chromosomes. cf. haploid.

distal
Part furthest away from the main part of the body. cf. proximal.

dorsal
The back or upper surface. cf. ventral.

ecdysis (ek-*digh*-sis)
Emergence of an insect from its old cuticle.

ecdysone (ek-*digh*-sohn)
Moulting hormone.

endocrine
Pertaining to the system producing hormones.

endophallus (end-oh-*fal*-us)
Penis.

epidermis (eppy-*der*-mis)
The living layer of cells at the base of the body wall.

epipharynx (eppy-*fa*-rincks)
Small pad of tissue behind the labrum acting as a seal when the proboscis is employed.

exocrine gland
Gland producing a substance which passes to the outside of the body.

fertilisation
Fusion of two gametes to produce a zygote.

flagellum (fla-*jell*-um)
Distal part of the antenna divided into 10 sections in the female castes and 11 in drones.

follicle
Structure incorporating a developing egg and its food cells.

gamete (*gam*-eet)
Reproductive cell.

ganglion (*gang*-lee-on)
Collection of nerve cells and their fibres forming a discrete structure.

gaster
All the abdomen behind the petiole, ie, the abdomen excluding the propodeum.

gene
Unit of inheritance found on a chromosome. Made of deoxyribonucleic acid (DNA).

genetics
Science of inheritance.

glossa
Central tubular structure of the proboscis down which the saliva passes.

glucose oxidase
Enzyme converting glucose to gluconic acid and hydrogen peroxide.

haemocyte (*heem*-oh-sight)
Any one of the cells making up part of the haemolymph (blood).

haemolymph (*heem*-oh-lymf)
Blood of the honey bee.

hamuli (*ham*-you-lee)
Hooks on the ventral edge of the hindwing which hook into a fold on the forewing when the bee is in flight.

haploid
Having a single set of unpaired chromosomes. cf. diploid.

hemizygous (hem-i-*zigh*-gus)
Having only one allelomorph of a pair or series.

heterozygous (*het*-er-oh-zigh-gus)
Carrying different allelomorphs at a particular chromosomal locus. cf. homozygous.

homozygous (*hoh*-moh-zigh-gus)
Carrying identical allelomorphs at a particular chromosomal locus. cf. heterozygous.

hormone
Substance produced in an endocrine gland and passed into the haemolymph.

Hymenoptera (high-men-*op*-terra)
Order of insects to which the honey bee belongs.

hypopharyngeal gland
(*high*-poh-fa-rin-jee-al gland)
One of a pair of glands in the head of the worker honey bee.

hypopharynx (high-poh-*fa*-rincks)
Structure at the base of the cibarium forming the floor of the cavity.

imago (im-*ar*-goh)
Adult honey bee.

invertase
Enzyme converting sucrose to glucose and fructose.

labellum (lab-*ell*-um)
Lobe at distal end of glossa. (*syn.* flabellum).

labium
Lower part of the insect mouthparts. In the honey bee forming part of the proboscis.

labrum (*lay*-brum)
Upper lip of the mouthparts.

lipoprotein (lip-oh-*proh*-teen)
Substance which is a complex of fat and protein.

Malpighian tubule (mal-*pig*-ee-an tubule)
One of the long, narrow, excretory structures of the honey bee.

mandibles
Paired biting parts of the adult honey bee's mouthparts.

maxilla
Secondary jaw, one of a pair, of an insect. In the adult honey bee forming part of the proboscis.

meiosis (migh-*oh*-sis)
Division of a nucleus when the number of chromosomes is halved. cf. mitosis.

mesothorax (*mee*-soh-thor-racks)
The second segment of the thorax.

metabolism (met-*ab*-ol-iz-um)
The sum of all the chemical reactions taking place inside an organism.

metamorphosis (metta-*morf*-os-is)
Change from the larval to adult form.

metathorax (*metta*-thor-racks)
The third segment of the thorax.

microvillus (migh-kroh-*vil*-us)
Extension from a cell, used to increase its surface area.

mitosis (migh-*toh*-sis)
Division of a nucleus when the original number of chromosomes is retained. cf. meiosis.

moulting
Separation of the old cuticle from the new one.

Nasonov gland (*naz*-on-ov gland)
Pheromone-producing gland under the tergum of A7.

neuron(e) (*new*-ron)
Nerve cell.

neurosecretory cell
(new-roh-sek-*reet*-or-ee cell)
Nerve cell able to secrete hormones.

notum
Alternative, and usual, name for a tergum in the thorax.

ocellus (oh-*sel*-us)
Simple eye.

oenocyte (*een*-oh-sight)
Cell found in the fat body and elsewhere, particularly the wax glands. Involved in production of lipoproteins.

oesophagus (ee-*sof*-a-gus)
Tube connecting the pharynx to the honey stomach.

ommatidium (om-a-*tid*-ee-um)
Individual structural unit of the compound eye.

ontogeny (ont-*oj*-on-ee)
History of the individual's development.

oocyte (oh-o-sight)
Structure which will develop into an egg.

ostium
An opening into the heart to allow the passage of haemolymph.

ovariole (oh-*vair*-ee-ohl)
Egg-producing tube in the ovary.

parthenogenesis
(*par*-then-oh-gen-is-is)
Sexual reproduction without fertilisation.

pedicel
Section of antenna between the scape and the flagellum.

peristalsis (perry-*stal*-sis)
Rhythmic contractions of muscles in the digestive system.

peritrophic membrane
(perry-*trofe*-ick membrane)
Gelatinous envelope surrounding the contents in the ventriculus.

petiole (*peet*-ee-ohl)
Narrow constriction between the propodeum and second abdominal segment.

phagocytosis (fag-oh-sight-*oh*-sis)
Method by which certain cells surround and ingest foreign bodies inside an organism.

phallotreme (*fal*-oh-treem)
Opening from the endophallus to the outside.

pharynx (*fa*-rincks)
Second part of the oral cavity of the honey bee, following, and continuous with, the cibarium.

pheromone (*fe*-ra-mohn)
Chemical produced by one honey bee which has an effect on the physiology, behaviour or development of another honey bee.

pleuron (*ploo*-ron)
A sclerite on the side of the thorax of the pupa and adult honey bee.

postcerebral glands (post-se-*reeb*-ral glands)
Glands found in the head, dorsal to the brain.

posterior
Back. cf. anterior.

proboscis (proh-*boss*-is)
Tubular structure through which food and saliva pass.

propodeum (prop-o-*dee*-um)
First abdominal segment, structurally forming part of the thorax.

propolis
Resins honey bees collect from tree buds and conifers.

proprioceptor (*proh*-pree-oh-sept-or)
Sense organ or nerve cell reacting to stimulus of movement within structures in the body.

prothorax
The first segment of the thorax, immediately behind the head.

protocerebrum
(proht-oh-se-*reeb*-rum)
Part of the brain derived from the front portion of the embryo brain.

proventriculus
(*proh*-vent-rick-you-lus)
Valve between the honey stomach and ventriculus.

proximal
Part nearest to the main part of the body. cf. distal.

rhodopsin (roh-*dop*-sin)
Pigment in the ommatidium reacting to light.

sclerite (*skle*-right)
Any one of the plates of cuticle making up the outer covering of the pupa and adult honey bee.

sclerotin (*skle*-rottin)
A hard substance mixed with chitin to strengthen the cuticle.

scape
Basal rigid stalk of the antenna, articulating with the head.

scolopale (*skol*-oh-pail)
Thin cap covering the dendrites in a sensillum.

scutellum (skoo-*tell*-um)
Small posterior part of the notum of the mesothorax.

scutum
Large anterior part of the notum of the mesothorax.

seminal vesicle (*sem*-in-al *vees*-ik-al)
Sperm-storing structure in the drone.

sensillum
Individual sense organ.

s. basiconicum (s. bay-si-*kon*-ee-kum)
Peg sense organ.

s. campaniformium (s. camp-an-i-*form*-ee-um)
Bell-shaped sense organ found in groups.

s. coeloconicum (s. seel-oh-*kon*-ee-kum)
Pit-peg sense organ

s. placodeum (s. plak-*oh*-dee-um)
Plate sense organ.

s. scolopophorusm (s. scohl-oh-*pof*-or-um)
Stretch receptor made of groups of sense organs joined together.

s. trichodeum (s. trigh-*koh*-dee-um)
Hair sense organ.

seta (*see*-ta)
A hair.

sinus (*sigh*-nus)
A space.

spermatheca (sperm-a-*theek*-a)
In the queen honey bee, a structure for storage of spermatozoa.

spermatozoon
Male reproductive cell.

spinneret
Opening from the silk glands.

spiracle (*spi*-rick-al)
An opening in the body wall of an insect allowing gases to flow in and out of the respiratory system.

sternum
A sclerite on the ventral side of the thorax and abdomen of the pupa and adult honey bee.

sulcus (*sulk*-us)
Groove in the cuticle marking the position of a ridge on the inside.

synapse (*sigh*-naps)
Microscopic gap between communicating neurons.

synergism
The increased effect of two substances working together.

taenidium (tie-*nid*-ee-um)
Spiral of cuticle surrounding and supporting the tracheae.

tarsomere (*tar*-soh-meer)
Any one of the divisions of the tarsus.

tegula (*teg*-yew-la)
Small flap of cuticle on the prothoracic notum of an adult bee, covering the first spiracle.

tergum
A sclerite on the dorsal side of the thorax and abdomen of the pupa and adult honey bee.

trachea (track-*ee*-a)
Tube forming part of the respiratory system and carrying gases.

tracheole (*track*-ee-ohl)
Tiny, thin-walled tubes forming the part of the respiratory system in contact with the tissues.

trichogen (*trigh*-koh-gen)
Producing a seta (hair).

tritocerebrum (tright-oh-se-*reeb*-rum)
Part of the brain derived from the hind part of the embryo brain and very small in the adult.

trochanter (troh-*kant*-a)
Second segment of a leg.

trophallaxis (trohf-al-*aks*-is)
Food sharing between individuals of a colony of honey bees.

trophocyte (*trofe*-oh-sight)
Cell relating to nutrition. Found, for example, in the fat body and the developing follicles.

ventral
The front or lower surface. cf. dorsal.

ventriculus (vent-*rick*-you-lus)
True stomach of the honey bee.

vesicle (*vee*-sik-al)
Bag-like container.

vitelline membrane (*vight*-el-leen)
Membrane surrounding the egg immediately inside the chorion.

zygote (*zigh*-goht)
Single cell produced by the fusion of two gametes.

REFERENCES AND FURTHER READING

Abercrombie, M., C. J. Hickman & M. L. Johnson. (1973) *The Penguin Dictionary of Biology*. Penguin Books Ltd, England.

Beetsma, J. (1979) 'The process of queen-worker differentiation in the honey bee'. *Bee World*, **60**(1), 24–39 (issued as a reprint by IBRA).

Birch, M. C. & K. F. Haynes. (1982) *Insect Pheromones*. Edward Arnold, London, UK.

Butler, C. G. (1954) *The World of the Honeybee*. Collins, London, UK.

Chapman, R. F. (1998) *The Insects: structure and function*. Cambridge University Press, Cambridge, UK.

Dade, H. A. (1977) *Anatomy and Dissection of the Honeybee*. International Bee Research Association, London, UK.

Davis, C. (2003) *Organisation of Colony Reproduction in the Honey Bee*. The Central Association of Bee-Keepers, UK.

Free, J. B. (ed) (1982) *Honey Bee Biology*. Central Association of Bee-Keepers, UK.

Free, J. B. (1987) *Pheromones of Social Bees*. Chapman & Hall, London, UK.

Frisch, K. von. (1950) *Bees: their vision, chemical senses and language*. Cornell University, Jonathan Cape Ltd, London, UK.

Goodman, L. (2003). *Form and Function in the Honey Bee*. International Bee Research Association, Cardiff, UK.

Gould, J. L. & C. G. Gould. (1995) *The Honey Bee*. Scientific American Library, WH Freeman & Co, New York, USA.

Hodges, D. (1952) *The Pollen Loads of the Honey Bee: a guide to their identification by colour and form*. Bee Research Association, London, UK.

Mobbs, P. G. (1981) *The Neural Regulation of Bee Behaviour*. The Central Association of Bee-Keepers, UK.

Morse, R. & T. Hooper. (1985) *The Illustrated Encyclopedia of Beekeeping*. Blandford Press, Poole, Dorset, UK.

Ribbands, R. (1953) *The Behaviour and Social Life of Honeybees*. Bee Research Association Ltd, London, UK.

Ross, H. H., C. A. Ross & J. R. P. Ross. (1982) *A Textbook of Entomology*. John Wiley & Sons Inc, New York, USA.

Seeley, Thomas D. (1995) *The Wisdom of the Hive*. Harvard University Press, Cambridge, MA, USA.

Snodgrass, R. E. (1956). *Anatomy of the Honey Bee*. Cornell University Press Ltd, London, UK.

Wigglesworth, V. B. (1972) *The Principles of Insect Physiology*. Chapman and Hall Ltd, London, UK.

Winston, M. (1987) *The Biology of the Honey Bee*. Harvard University Press, Cambridge, MA, USA.

INDEX

Numbers in **bold** type refer to diagrams/photographs.

and respiratory system, 36
mouth, 9, 25, 26, 51, **86**
mouthparts, 3, 6-11, 21-2, 49, 51,
52
development of, 84, 85, 86, 88
muscles, 39, 43, 48-51 *passim*, 53,
73
circulatory system and, 31, 32
development of, 82, 84, 88, 89
digestive system and, 26-8
passim
drone, 23, 75, 76, 78
heat production by, 127
respiration and, 36, 37
stinging and, 19-20
muscles, flight, 15-17, 23, 75, 88,
105, 128, 130

nectar, 97, 98, 107, 108, 112,
132-4, 135-6
processing, 41, 133-4
transport of, 27, 133
use by colony, 42, 112, 119-20,
128, 129, 131
nectaries, 132
nerve cells, *see* neurons
nerve cord, ventral, 31, 46-9, 84

nerves, 37, 44, 46, 49, 60, 89
nervous system, 43-58, 59, 60, 82,
86
neuron, 44-6, 47, 50-3, 54, 55, 56,
57, 59
neurosecretory cells, 58-9
notum, *see* tergum

ocelli, 21, 22, 23, 53, **54**, 57-8, 85
oenocytes, 29, 30, 41, 42, 72, 82,
86
oesophagus, 25, 27, 28, 59
oil, 29
see also fat
ommatidium, 54-7
ontogeny, 94
ostia, 32
ova, *see* eggs
ovaries, 71, 72-3, 74, 75, 86
oxygen, 30, 33, 34, 35, 36, 39

parthenogenesis, 68
patrolling, 94, 95-6, 105
penis, *see* endophallus
peristalsis, 27
peritrophic membrane, 27-8

petiole, 4-5, 32, 121
phagocytosis, 34
pharynx, 10, 25, 26, 27, 32
pheromones, 40, 97-102, 117, 118
alarm, 41, 95, 100, 108-9
brood, 74, 100
footprint, 101
Nasonov, 100-1, 114
queen mandibular (queen
substance), 74, 79, 100-1,
111-12, 113-14
queen tarsal, 112
sting, 95, 100-2, 109
tergite gland, 79
piping, 105, 117-18
plasma, 32-3, 38
pleuron, 3-4
poisoning, 110
pollen, 27, 112, 124, 132, 136-7
collection of, 12, 14-15, 22
use in colony, 91, 94-5, 96, 98,
120, 131, 136-7
pollen basket, *see* corbicula
pollen press, **12**, 14
predators of honey bee colonies,
106, 109, 115
prepupa, 29, 87
pre-oral cavity, 7, 9
proboscis, 9-10, 22, 23, 75, 97,
108, 132-4 *passim*
proctiger, 28
proctodeum, *see* hindgut
procuticle, 2, 6
propodeum, 4, 36, 37
propolis, 12, 15, 22, 122, 132, 138
proprioceptor, 49, 53
protein, 27, 33, 60, 98, 136-7
breakdown, 38
in fat bodies, 29-30, 88, 131
in yolk, 72
proventriculus, 25, 26, 27, 28, 133
pupa, 28-30 *passim*, 75-6, 85,
87-90, **117**, 130

queen, **21**, 22-3, 62, 67-9, 70, 73,
99-100
cell, 90, 112
cup, **112**
development of, 90-2
egg-laying rate of, 98, 124-5
piping, 105
pseudo, 74
rearing, 101, 112
reproductive system of, 70-4

virgin, 117, 119
see also caste determination;
mating
queen substance, *see under*
pheromones

races of bee
African, 74, 107, 110
Cape (*Apis mellifera capensis*), 74
European, 74
rectum, **25**, **26**, 28, 40, **71**
reproduction, 60, 61, 70-80
colony, *see* swarming
reproductive systems, 82, 84, 89
drone, 75-8
queen, 70-4
worker, 74
respiration, 35-8
cellular, 34, 56
respiratory system, 34-8, 86
rhabdom, 55, 57
rhodopsin, 55-6
robbing, 95, 103, 108-10
royal jelly, 40, 91-2, 95

saliva, 27, 120
salivary glands, *see* labial glands
salts, 33, 38, 39
sclerite, 3, 37
sclerotin, 2-3
scout bees, 112, 115-17
segmentation, 3-4, 47, 84, 85
sense organs, 44, 45, 48, 49-53, 75,
82, 121
see also eyes; sensilla
sensilla, 50-3, 89, 128
basiconica, 51
campaniformia, 52
coeloconica, 52
placodea, 52
scolopophora (chordotonal
organs), 52-3
trichodea, 50-1, 53
sex determination, 62, 68-70, 73
sight, 49, 50, 53-8, 79
silk, 87
sinuses, dorsal and ventral, 29, 31
smell, sense of, 49, 51-2, 53, 98,
107, 109
sound, perception of, 49, 53
spermatheca, **71**, 72, 74, 80
spermatozoa (sperm), 61, 64, 68,
75, 76
development of, 73, 84